Illuminate
Publishing

D0232412

WJEC

AS Human Biology

Study and Revision Guide

Gareth Rowlands

ip

Published in 2013 by Illuminate Publishing Ltd, P.O Box 1160, Cheltenham, Gloucestershire GL50 9RW

Orders: Please visit www.illuminatepublishing.com
or email sales@illuminatepublishing.com

British Library Cataloguing in Publication Data

A catalogue record for this book is available from the British Library

ISBN 978-1-908682-12-3

Printed by 4edge Ltd, Hockley, Essex.

02.13

The publisher's policy is to use papers that are natural, renewable and recyclable products made from wood grown in sustainable forests. The logging and manufacturing processes are expected to conform to the environmental regulations of the country of origin.

Every effort has been made to contact copyright holders of material reproduced in this book. If notified, the publishers will be pleased to rectify any errors or omissions at the earliest opportunity.

Editor: Geoff Tuttle

Design and layout: Nigel Harriss

Permissions

cover: ©Fotolia; TheSupe87
© Shutterstock: p51, photobar; p81, Levent Konuk; p91, Alila Sao Mai; p97, sergei telegin; p102, Blamb; p103, Henrik Larsson

WJEC examination questions are reproduced by permission from WJEC

Acknowledgements

I am very grateful to the team at Illuminate Publishing for their professionalism, support and guidance throughout this project. It has been a pleasure to work so closely with them.

The author and publisher wish to thank:

Dr John Ford and Dr Marianne Izen for their thorough review of the book and expert insights and observations.

Contents

How to use this book   4

Knowledge and Understanding

BY1 **Basic Biochemistry and Cell Structure   6**

Biochemistry   8

Cell structure and organisation   15

Cell surface membrane   20

Transport across cell membranes   21

Enzymes   26

Nucleic acids   32

Cell division   34

HB2 **Biodiversity and Physiology of Body Systems 44**

Biodiversity and evolution   46

Uptake of energy and nutrients   56

Gas exchange   65

Transport to and from exchange surfaces   72

Human defence mechanisms   90

Pathogens, the spread of human disease
and the control of infection   99

Exam Practice and Technique

Exam practice and skills   120

Questions and answers   123

Quickfire answers   143

Exam practice answers   146

Index   150

How to use this book

As a former Principal Examiner I have written this study guide to help you be aware of what is required, and structured the content to guide you through to success in the WJEC Human Biology AS level examination.

Knowledge and Understanding

The **first section** of the book covers the key knowledge required for the examination.

There are notes for the compulsory sections of each examination:

BY1 – Basic Biochemistry and Cell Structure

HB2 – Biodiversity and Physiology of Body Systems.

At the end of each unit there are a number of practice exam questions from past WJEC A Level Biology and Human Biology exam papers. These are designed to help you practise for the exams and reinforce what you have learned. Answers are included at the end of the book.

In addition, I have tried to give you additional pointers so that you can develop your work:

- Any of the terms in the WJEC specification can be used as the basis of a question, so I have highlighted those terms and offered definitions.

- There are 'Quickfire' questions designed to test your knowledge and understanding of the material.

- I have offered examination advice based on experience of what candidates need to do to attain the highest grades.

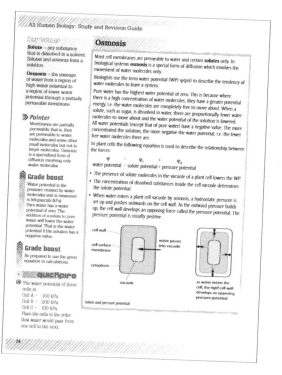

Exam Practice and Technique

The **second section** of the book covers the key skills for examination success and offers you examples based on real-life responses to examination questions. First you will be guided into an understanding of how the examination system works, and then offered clues to success.

A variety of structured and essay questions are provided in this section. Each essay includes the marking points expected followed by actual samples of candidates' responses. A variety of structured questions are also provided, together with typical responses and comments. They offer a guide as to the standard that is required, and the commentary will explain why the responses gained the marks that they did.

Most importantly, I advise that you should take responsibility for your own learning and not rely on your teachers to give you notes or tell you how to gain the grades that you require. You should look for additional notes to support your study into WJEC Human Biology.

I advise that you look at the WJEC website www.wjec.co.uk. In particular, you need to be aware of the specification. Look for specimen examination papers and mark schemes. You may find past papers useful as well.

Good luck with your revision.

Gareth Rowlands

Knowledge and Understanding

BY1 Basic Biochemistry and Cell Structure

The BY1 unit incorporates biochemistry and cell structure which is fundamental to the functioning of living organisms. The function of molecules depends on their properties. A molecule gets its properties from its structure. A knowledge of basic cell structure is essential in the understanding of the transport mechanisms involved in the exchange of molecules between the cell and its surroundings. In cells metabolic reactions take place rapidly involving thousands of simultaneous reactions. Order and control is essential if reactions are to be prevented from interfering with each other. These features of metabolism are made possible by the action of enzymes. Chromosomes are made up mainly of DNA. Genetic information needs to be copied and passed on to the daughter cells by the process of cell division known as mitosis.

Revision checklist

Tick column 1 when you have completed brief revision notes.
Tick column 2 when you think you have a good grasp of the topic.
Tick column 3 during final revision when you feel you have mastery of the topic.

		1	2	3	Notes
	Biochemistry				
p8	Carbohydrates				
p10	Lipids				
p12	Proteins				
p13	Water				
	Cell structure and organisation				
p15	Cell organisation				
p16	Cell structure				
	Cell surface membrane				
p20	Membrane structure				
p21	The membrane as a barrier				
	Transport across cell membranes				
p21	Diffusion				
p22	Facilitated diffusion				
p23	Active transport				
p24	Osmosis				

		1	2	3	Notes
Enzymes					
p26	Enzyme structure				
p27	Factors affecting the rate of enzyme action				
p29	Enzyme inhibition				
p30	Medical and industrial applications of enzymes				
Nucleic acids					
p32	The structure of DNA				
p33	The structure of RNA				
Cell division					
p34	Mitosis				
p36	Meiosis				
p36	Comparison of mitosis and meiosis				

Grade boost

You should be able to recognise and understand structural formulae but not reproduce them. However, be prepared to use structural formulae if they are provided in an exam question.

quickfire

① With reference to carbohydrates explain the difference between a condensation reaction and hydrolysis.

α-glucose

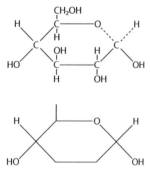

Molecular structure of α glucose.

Biochemistry

Carbohydrates

Carbohydrates are organic compounds containing the elements carbon, hydrogen and oxygen. Many organic molecules, including carbohydrates, are made up of a chain of individual molecules each of which is given the general name monomer. Polymers are longer chains of repeating monomer units. In carbohydrates the basic monomer unit is called a monosaccharide. Two monosaccharides combine to form a disaccharide.

Many monosaccharide molecules combine to form a polysaccharide.

Monosaccharides

Monosaccharides are relatively small organic molecules and provide the building blocks for the larger carbohydrates. Monosaccharides have the general formula $(CH_2O)n$ and their name is determined by the number of carbon atoms in the molecule (n). A triose sugar has three carbon atoms, a pentose sugar five carbon atoms. Glucose is a hexose sugar.

All hexose sugars share the formula $C_6H_{12}O_6$ but they differ in their molecular structure. Monosaccharides usually exist as ring structures when dissolved in water. Glucose exists as two **isomers**, the α form and the β form. These different forms result in considerable biological differences when they form polymers such as starch and cellulose.

Disaccharides

Disaccharides consist of two monosaccharide units linked together with the formation of a glycosidic bond *and the elimination of water*. This is called a condensation reaction. Disaccharides can be formed by the joining of two similar monosaccharides or by the joining of two different monosaccharides.

Glucose joined to glucose forms maltose.

Glucose joined to fructose forms sucrose.

Glucose joined to galactose forms lactose.

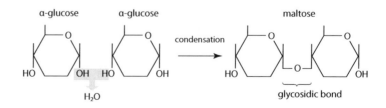

Formation of a glycosidic bond when two glucose molecules combine to form maltose.

Polysaccharides

Polysaccharides are an example of large, complex molecules called polymers. They are formed from very large numbers of monosaccharide units linked together by glycosidic bonds.

Starch is a storage polysaccharide found in plant cells in the form of starch grains. These are found in seeds and storage organs such as potato tubers. Starch is made up of many α glucose molecules held together. It is an ideal storage molecule because it is compact and can be stored in a small space; is insoluble and does not draw water towards it by osmosis.

Starch is made up of two polymers, amylose and amylopectin. Amylose is linear (unbranched) and coils into a helix, whereas amylopectin is branched and fits inside the amylose.

The main storage product in animals is called glycogen, sometimes called animal starch and is very similar to amylopectin. Both starch and glycogen are readily hydrolysed to α glucose, which is soluble and can then be transported to areas where energy is needed.

Cellulose is a structural polysaccharide and is a major component of plant cell walls.

Cellulose consists of many long parallel chains of β glucose molecules cross-linked to each other by hydrogen bonds. Being made up of β glucose units, the chain has adjacent glucose molecules rotated by 180°. This allows hydrogen bonds to be formed between the hydroxyl groups of adjacent parallel chains and helps to give cellulose its structural stability. These chains are grouped together into microfibrils a number of which are arranged in parallel groups called fibres. The large number of hydrogen bonds present contribute to the strength and rigidity of plant cell walls.

Chitin is a polysaccharide found in insects. It is similar to cellulose but has amino acids added to form a mucopolysaccharide. It is strong, waterproof and lightweight and forms the exoskeleton of insects.

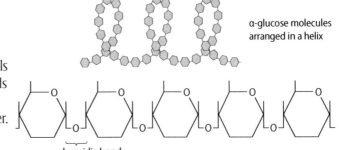

α-glucose molecules arranged in a helix

glycosidic bond

Structure of a molecule of starch.

>> **Pointer**

All monosaccharides and some disaccharides, such as maltose, are reducing sugars. Describe the Benedict's test for a reducing sugar. How does the test for a non-reducing sugar, such as sucrose, differ?

Grade boost

In β glucose units the positions of the –H group and the –OH group on carbon atom C1 are reversed. In β glucose the –OH group is above, rather than below. This means that to form glycosidic links each β glucose molecule must be rotated by 180° compared to the one next to it.

quickfire

② State whether these carbohydrates are mono-, di-, or polysaccharides and give each their role in living organisms. State whether each occurs in plants, animals or both: lactose, cellulose, glucose, glycogen.

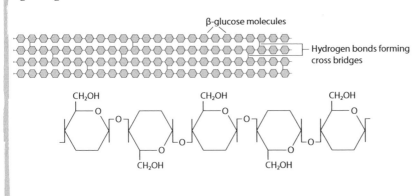

β-glucose molecules

Hydrogen bonds forming cross bridges

Structure of a molecule of cellulose.

Key Term

Polar = charged molecules that have two ends or poles that interact differently to water and fat. A hydrophilic head is attracted to water but not to fat, whereas a hydrophobic tail mixes readily with fat but is repelled by water.

③ Name the products formed and the type of bond that is broken when a triglyceride is broken down.

quickfire

④ Suggest why parts of organisms that move, such as seeds, use lipids as an energy store rather than carbohydrates.

quickfire

⑤ What is meant by metabolic water?

Lipids

Fats

Like carbohydrates, lipids also contain carbon, hydrogen and oxygen but in proportion to the carbon and hydrogen they contain less oxygen. They are **non-polar** compounds and so are insoluble in water.

Triglycerides are formed by condensation reactions between glycerol and fatty acids. A triglyceride consists of one molecule of glycerol and three fatty acid molecules. In this reaction, water is removed and an oxygen bond, known as an ester bond, is formed between the glycerol and fatty acid.

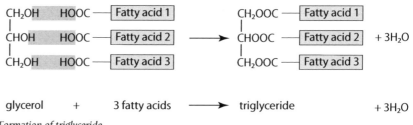

Formation of triglyceride.

The glycerol molecule is always the same but there are many different fatty acids that might react with glycerol. There are of two main kinds of fatty acids:

- Saturated fatty acids where all the carbon atoms are joined by a single bond.
- Unsaturated fatty acids contain one or more double bonds and therefore have fewer hydrogen atoms than they might.

A high intake of fat, notably saturated fats, is a contributory factor in heart disease.

Chemical properties

- They are insoluble in water but dissolve in organic solvents such as acetone/propanone and alcohols.
- Fats are solid at room temperature, whereas oils, which are unsaturated lipids, are liquids.

Functions

- Energy storage. Fats are an efficient energy store in both plants and animals. One gram of fat when oxidised yields approximately twice as much energy as the same mass of carbohydrate.
- Triglycerides also produce a lot of metabolic water when oxidised. This is important in desert animals such as the camel.
- Protection of delicate internal organs such as kidneys.
- Insulation. Fats are poor conductors of heat and when stored under the skin, they help retain body heat.
- Waterproofing. Fats are insoluble in water and are important in land organisms such as insects where the waxy cuticle cuts down water loss. Leaves also have a waxy cuticle to reduce transpiration.

Phospholipids

Phospholipids are important in the formation and functioning of membranes in cells. They are similar to triglycerides with one of the fatty acid groups replaced by a phosphate group.

- The lipid part is non-polar and insoluble in water (**hydrophobic**).
- The phosphate group is **polar** and dissolves in water (**hydrophilic**).

Phospholipids allow lipid-soluble substances to enter and leave a cell and prevent water-soluble substances entering and leaving the cell.

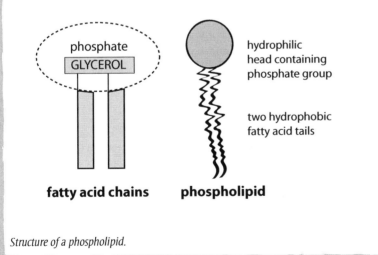

Structure of a phospholipid.

Key Terms

Hydrophilic = attracts water.

Hydrophobic = repels water.

quickfire

⑥ State two differences between a triglyceride and a phospholipid.

quickfire

⑦ Which end of the phospholipid molecule lies to the outside of the membrane?

quickfire

⑧ State through which part of the membrane each of the following passes in order to enter or leave a cell:
1. Sodium ion.
2. A lipid soluble molecule.

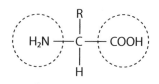

Structural formula of a generalised amino acid.

≫ Pointer

Proteins carry out a range of biological activities and include enzymes, antibodies, hormones, carrier and transport proteins, as well as structural proteins.

≫ Pointer

Make sure you are familiar with the different bonds involved in each of the different levels of protein structure.

≫ Pointer

Each protein is different because of its 3D shape. This allows the protein to recognise and be recognised by other molecules, for example the combination of enzymes and substrates.

quickfire

⑨ List the four bonds present in the tertiary structure of a protein.

Tertiary structure of protein.

Proteins

- Proteins differ from carbohydrates and lipids in that in addition to carbon, hydrogen and oxygen, they always contain nitrogen. Many proteins also contain sulphur and sometimes phosphorus.
- Proteins are large compounds built up of sub-units called amino acids. About 20 different amino acids are used to make up proteins. There are thousands of different proteins and their shape is determined by the specific sequence of amino acids in the chain.
- All amino acids have the same basic structure in that each possesses an amino group, $-NH_2$, at one end of the molecule, and a carboxyl group, $-COOH$, at the other end. It is the R group which differs from one amino acid to another.

The peptide bond

Proteins are built up from a linear sequence of amino acids. The amino group of one amino acid reacts with the carboxyl group of another with the elimination of water. The bond that is formed is called a peptide bond and the resulting compound is a dipeptide. A number of amino acids joined in this way is called a polypeptide.

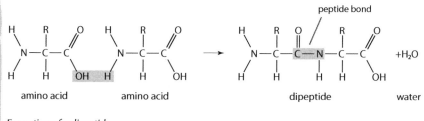

Formation of a dipeptide.

Protein structure

Four levels of protein structure exist:

1. The primary structure of a protein is the sequence of amino acid in its polypeptide chain. The proteins differ from each other in the variety, numbers and orders of their constituent amino acids linked by peptide bonds only.
2. The secondary structure is the shape that the polypeptide chain forms as a result of hydrogen bonding. This is most often a spiral known as the α helix. An alternative is a pleated sheet occurring as a flat zig-zag chain.
3. The tertiary structure is formed by the bending and twisting of the polypeptide helix into a compact structure. This gives the molecule its 3D shape. The shape is maintained by disulphide, ionic and hydrogen bonds.
4. The quaternary structure arises from a combination of two or more polypeptide chains in tertiary form. These are associated with non-protein groups and form large, complex molecules, e.g. haemoglobin.

Classification of proteins

Proteins can be divided into two groups according to their structure:

- Fibrous proteins perform structural functions. They consist of polypeptides in parallel chains or sheets with numerous cross-linkages to form long fibres. For example, keratin (in hair). Fibrous proteins are insoluble in water, strong and tough. Collagen provides tough properties needed in tendons. A single fibre consists of three polypeptide chains twisted around each other like a rope. These chains are linked by cross-bridges making a very stable molecule.

- Globular proteins perform a variety of different functions – enzymes, antibodies, plasma proteins and hormones. These proteins are compact and folded as spherical molecules. They are soluble in water. Haemoglobin consists of four folded polypeptide chains, at the centre of each of which is an iron-containing group called haem.

Inorganic ions

Inorganic ions play important roles in living organisms. In plants, mineral ions are transported dissolved in water. They can be divided into two groups:

- Macronutrients which are needed in small amounts. These include:
  - Magnesium, a constituent of chlorophyll in leaves.
  - Iron, a constituent of haemoglobin in blood.
  - Phosphate, found in the plasma membrane, nucleic acids, ATP.
  - Calcium, a constituent of bones and teeth.
- Micronutrients which are needed in minute (trace) amounts, e.g. copper, zinc.

Water

Apart from providing a habitat for aquatic organisms, water plays an important role in plants and animals with key elements found in aqueous solution. Water is transparent, allowing light to pass through, enabling aquatic plants to photosynthesise effectively.

Water acts as a medium for metabolic reactions. Water makes up between 65% and 95% by mass of most plants and animals. It is an important constituent of cells. The hydrophobic property of lipids is important in cell membranes.

>> **Pointer**

You should be able to use given structural formulae (proteins, triglycerides and carbohydrates) to show how bonds are formed and broken by condensation and hydrolysis, including peptide, glycosidic and ester bonds.

 **quickfire**

(10) Classify the following proteins as fibrous or globular: insulin, collagen, keratin, lysozyme (an enzyme).

Grade boost

You are required to learn the functions of these four elements:
Magnesium
Iron
Phosphate
Calcium.

>> **Pointer**

Compare a polypeptide to a piece of string. In a fibrous protein several strands are twisted together like a rope, whereas in a globular protein the string is rolled into a ball.

Grade boost

A molecule gets its properties from its structure. Be prepared to explain how the properties of water enable it to carry out its many important roles in living organisms.

⑪ Why is water described as a polar molecule?

⑫ State the properties of water which allow the following:
How are insects able to walk on water?
How are fish able to live in a frozen pond?
Why does sweating keep us cool?

⑬ Why are the following properties of water important to living organisms?
1. It is a universal solvent.
2. It is transparent.

Cohesion and surface tension

- Water is a polar molecule and has no overall charge. The oxygen end of the molecule has a slight negative charge and the hydrogen end of the molecule has a slight positive charge. When two water molecules are in close contact their opposing charges attract each other forming a hydrogen bond. Individually the hydrogen bonds are weak but because there are many of them they stick together in a strong lattice framework. This sticking together of water molecules is called cohesion. This means that tall columns of water can be drawn up xylem vessels in tall trees.

- At ordinary temperatures water has the highest surface tension of any liquid except mercury. In a pond the cohesion between water molecules produces surface tension so that the body of an insect such as the pond skater is supported.

Water as a solvent

- Because water is a polar molecule it will attract other charged particles, such as ions, and other polar molecules, such as glucose. This allows chemical reactions to take place in solution and since these chemicals dissolve in water, it acts a transport medium, e.g. in animals blood transports many dissolved substances. In plants water transports minerals in the xylem and sucrose in the phloem. Non-polar molecules such as lipids will not dissolve in water.

Thermal properties

- Water has a high specific heat. A large amount of heat energy is needed to raise the temperature of water. This is because the hydrogen bonds between water molecules restrict their movement. This prevents large fluctuations in the temperature of water and this is particularly important in keeping the temperature of aquatic habitats stable so that organisms do not have to endure extremes of temperature. This also allows enzymes within the cells to work effectively.

- Water has a high latent heat, i.e. a great deal of heat energy is needed to change it from a liquid to a vapour state. This is important, for example, in temperature control where heat is used for vaporisation of water when sweating. That is, the evaporation of water from a surface results in cooling.

Density

- Water has a maximum density at 4°C. Water in its solid form (ice) is less dense than water and so floats on the surface. Ice forms an insulating layer and allows organisms to survive beneath it.

Cell structure and organisation

Cell organisation

There are two types of cell: prokaryotic cells and eukaryotic cells. Prokaryote cells have a simple structure and were probably the first forms of life on Earth. Eukaryotic cells probably evolved from prokaryote cells around 1000 million years ago.

An example of a prokaryote cell is a bacterium. Eukaryote cells are typical of the great majority of organisms including all animals and plants.

Prokaryotic cells	Eukaryotic cells
Found in bacteria and blue-green algae	Found in plants, animals, fungi and protoctists
No membrane-bound organelles	Membrane-bound organelles
DNA lies free in the cytoplasm	DNA located on chromosomes
No nuclear membrane or ER	Distinct membrane-bound nucleus
Ribosomes are smaller	Ribosomes are larger
Cell wall containing murein	Cell wall in plants made of cellulose

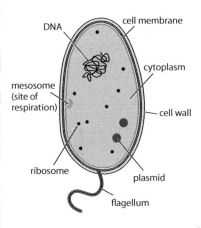

Structure of a generalised bacterial cell.

Viruses

Viruses cause a variety of infectious diseases in humans, animals and plants. Viruses are extremely small and can only be seen using an electron microscope. They can be called 'non-cells' as they have no cytoplasm, no organelles and no chromosomes. Outside a living cell a virus exists as an inert 'virion'. When they invade a cell they are able to take over the cell's metabolism and multiply within the host cell. Each virus particle is made up of a core of nucleic acid surrounded by a protein coat, the capsid. Most viruses are found in animal cells and those attacking bacteria (bacteriophages) have the nucleic acid DNA. Other animal and plant viruses contain RNA. A widely studied virus is T2 phage, a bacteriophage, which infects the bacterium *Escherichia coli (E.coli)*

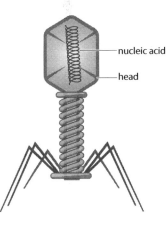

A virus.

⑭ What are the two major components of a virus?

Cell structure

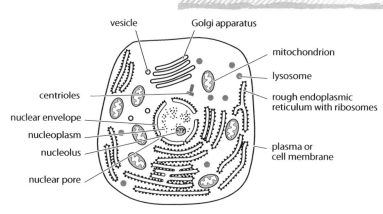

vesicle
Golgi apparatus
mitochondrion
lysosome
rough endoplasmic reticulum with ribosomes
centrioles
nuclear envelope
nucleoplasm
nucleolus
plasma or cell membrane
nuclear pore

Generalised structure of an animal cell as seen using an electron microscope.

Grade boost

You should be able to recognise organelles in electron micrographs.

Grade boost

Compare the cell structure of eukaryote, animal and plant, prokaryote and virus.

≫ Pointer

The cell is a 3D structure. An electron micrograph may show mitochondria as circular or sausage-shaped as they are cut in different planes.

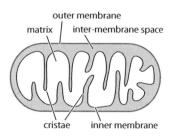

outer membrane
matrix
inter-membrane space
cristae
inner membrane

Basic structure of a mitochondrion.

The cell is the basic unit of life and each cell can be thought of as a separate place where chemical processes of that cell take place. Simple organisms consist of only one cell, that is, they are unicellular. More advanced organisms consist of many cells and are said to be multicellular, where different cells are specialised to carry our particular functions. Plant and animal cells contain a number of organelles that perform a variety of functions. The electron microscope enables scientists to view the detailed structure of these organelles. This is known as the ultrastructure of the cell.

The cytoplasm is a highly organised material consisting of a soluble ground substance called the cytosol in which are found a variety of organelles.

Nucleus

This is the most prominent feature in the cell. Its function is to control the cell's activities and to retain the chromosomes. The nucleus is bounded by a double membrane, the nuclear membrane (or envelope). This has pores in it to allow the transport of mRNA. The cytoplasm-like material within the nucleus is called the nucleoplasm. It contains chromatin, which is made up of coils of DNA bound to protein (histones). During cell division the chromatin condenses to form the chromosomes. Within the nucleus is a small spherical body called a nucleolus. Its function is to manufacture RNA which is needed to make ribosomes.

Mitochondrion

The mitochondrion has a double membrane separated by a narrow fluid-filled inter-membrane space. The inner membrane is folded inwards to form extensions called cristae. The interior of the mitochondrion contains an organic matrix containing numerous chemical compounds. Mitochondria are the sites of aerobic respiration in the cell. Some of the reactions take place in the matrix while others occur on the inner membrane. The cristae increase the surface area on which the respiratory processes take place. The function of mitochondria is to produce energy as ATP. Muscle cells contain large numbers of mitochondria, reflecting the high metabolic activity taking place there.

Endoplasmic reticulum (ER)

This consists of an elaborate system of parallel double membranes forming flattened sacs. The fluid-filled spaces between the membranes are called cisternae. The ER is connected with the nuclear membrane and may link to the Golgi body. The cavities are interconnected and this system allows the transport of materials throughout the cell. There are two types of ER:

- Rough ER has ribosomes on the outer surface. The rough ER functions in transporting proteins made by the ribosomes. Rough ER is present in large amounts in cells that make enzymes that may be secreted out of the cell.

- Smooth ER has membranes which lack ribosomes. These are concerned with the synthesis and transport of lipids.

Ribosomes

These are made up of one large and one small sub-unit. They are manufactured in the nucleolus from ribosomal RNA and protein. They are important in protein synthesis.

Golgi body

This is similar in structure to ER but is more compact. The Golgi body is formed by rough ER being pinched off at the ends to form small vesicles. A number of these vesicles then fuse together to form the Golgi body. Proteins are transported in the vesicles and are modified and packaged in the Golgi body. For example, proteins may be combined with carbohydrates to make glycoproteins. At the other end of the Golgi body vesicles can be pinched off and the products secreted by **exocytosis** when the vesicle moves to and fuses with the cell membrane.

Other functions of the Golgi body include:

- Producing secretory enzymes.
- Secreting carbohydrates, e.g. for the formation of plant cell walls.
- Producing glycoprotein.
- Transporting and storing lipids.
- Forming lysosomes.

Key term

Exocytosis = process by which a substance leaves a cell after being transported through the cytoplasm in a vesicle.

Grade boost

Membranous organelles are enclosed areas within the cytoplasm. This has advantages in that potentially harmful chemicals and/or enzymes can be isolated. Membranes also provide a large surface area for the attachment of enzymes involved in metabolic processes, as well as providing a transport system within the cell.

Pointer

Once you have used the term 'endoplasmic reticulum' it is acceptable to abbreviate to 'ER'.

quickfire

⑮ The following are functions of different organelles. Name the organelle in each case:
  1. Protein synthesis.
  2. Producing glycoproteins.
  3. Producing ATP.
  4. Producing ribosomes.

Grade boost

Do not consider organelles in isolation. Find out how the following pairs of organelles are linked. Nucleolus and ribosomes; rough ER, vesicle and Golgi body.

Grade boost

Each organelle has a particular function. It is possible to work out the role of some cells by observing the number and size of the organelles it contains. For example, a muscle cell requires a lot of ATP and so contains many mitochondria.

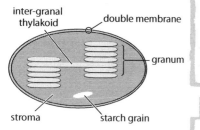

inter-granal thylakoid — double membrane

granum

stroma — starch grain

Basic structure of a chloroplast.

⑯ Name the organelle in each case that possesses the following structures:
1. Cristae.
2. Thylakoids.
3. Cisternae.

Lysosomes

Lysosomes are small vacuoles formed when portions of the Golgi body are pinched off. They contain and isolate digestive enzymes from the remainder of the cell. They can also release these enzymes and destroy worn out organelles in the cell. Digestion is carried out in the membrane-lined vacuole into which several lysosomes may discharge their contents.

They can also digest material that has been taken into the cell, e.g. white blood cells engulf bacteria by **phagocytosis** and the lysosomes discharge their contents into the vesicle so formed and digest the bacterium.

Centrioles

Centrioles are found in all animal cells but are absent from the cells of higher plants. Centrioles are located just outside the nucleus in a distinct region of the cytoplasm known as the centrosome. A centriole consists of two hollow cylinders positioned at right angles to one another. During cell division centrioles divide and move to opposite poles of the cell where they synthesise the microtubules of the spindle.

Chloroplast

Chloroplasts are found in the cells of photosynthesising tissue. They have a double membrane inside which is the fluid stroma, containing ribosomes, lipid, circular DNA and possibly starch. Within the stroma are a number of flattened sacs called thylakoids. A stack of thylakoids is called a granum.

Each granum consists of between two and a hundred of these closed, parallel, flattened sacs. The photosynthetic pigments such as chlorophyll are found within the thylakoids. This arrangement produces a large surface area for trapping light energy.

Vacuole

Plant cells have a large permanent vacuole which consists of a fluid-filled sac bounded by a single membrane, the tonoplast. Vacuoles contain cell sap, a storage site for chemicals such as glucose, and provide an osmotic system which functions in support of young tissues.

Animal cells contain vacuoles but these are small, temporary vesicles and may occur in large numbers.

Cellulose cell wall

The cell wall consists of cellulose microfibrils embedded in a polysaccharide matrix. The main functions of a cell wall are:
- To provide strength and support.
- To permit the movement of water from cell to cell.

Differences between plant and animal cells

Plant cells have all the structures found in animal cells plus some additional features:

Plant cells	Animal cells
Cell wall	No cell wall
Chloroplasts	No chloroplasts
Large permanent vacuole	Small, temporary vacuoles
No **centrioles**	Centrioles
Plasmodesmata	No plasmodesmata

Levels of organisation

Unicellular organisms carry out all life functions within a single cell.

Multicellular organisms are more efficient as they contain a variety of different cells. As they develop, each cell becomes specialised in structure to suit the role it will perform. This is called cell differentiation. For example, nerve cells become long and thin to carry impulses. Some cells remain undifferentiated and function as 'packing' cells, for example parenchyma cells in plants.

Tissues

Cells are usually grouped together. A tissue consists of a collection of similar cells that carry out a particular function, for example epithelial tissue. These are sheets of cells that line the surface of organs in animals. These cells often have a protective or secretory function.

Just as cells are grouped into tissues, different tissues are aggregated into organs.

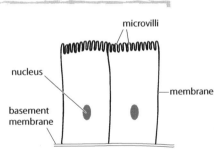

Epithelial cells from the lining of the small intestine.

- An organ is composed of several different tissues that are coordinated to perform a function, for example the eye.
- Organs work together as a single unit or organ system, for example the digestive system.
- Consequently organisms are made up of a number of different systems that work together.

Key Terms

Centriole = structure in cell division from which spindle fibres develop.

Plasmodesmata = strands of cytoplasm linking cells together.

⑰ List three features present in a plant cell, not found in an animal cell.

⑱ State whether each of the following is a cell, tissue or organ:
kidney, epithelium, muscle, sperm.

Cell surface membrane

Membrane structure

The cell surface membrane or plasma membrane is the boundary that separates the living cell from its surroundings. The membrane also controls which substances pass into and out of the cell. The cell membrane is made up almost entirely of proteins and phospholipids.

The phosphate head of the phospholipid is a polar molecule (hydrophilic or water-loving) and has an attraction for other polar molecules such as water. The fatty acid end of the phospholipid, made up of two fatty acid tails, is non-polar (hydrophobic or water-hating) and repels water. Phospholipids can form bilayers with one sheet of phospholipid forming over another. This phospholipid bilayer forms the basis of membrane structure. The use of the electron microscope enabled Singer and Nicolson to put forward their theory called the Fluid Mosaic model in 1972. They proposed that:

- There is a **bimolecular** phospholipid layer (bilayer).
- Associated with the bilayer is a variety of protein molecules:
  - Extrinsic proteins which occur on the surface of the bilayer or partly embedded in it.
  - Intrinsic proteins which extend across both layers.
- The phospholipid layer is capable of movement, i.e. it is fluid and in surface view the proteins are dotted throughout the bilayer in a mosaic arrangement.

The model is referred to as the 'Fluid Mosaic' model because the components are free to move with respect to each other and the proteins embedded in the bilayer vary in shape, size and pattern.

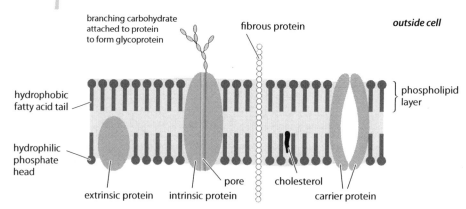

Fluid Mosaic model of the cell membrane.

Cholesterol is also found in animal cells. It fits between the phospholipid molecules, increasing the rigidity and stability of the membrane. Glycolipids (lipids that have combined with polysaccharide) are also found in the outer layer of the membrane and are thought to be involved in cell-to-cell recognition. Glycoproteins also stick out of some membranes.

The main functions of the proteins in the cell membrane include:

- Providing structural support.
- Allowing active transport across the membrane by forming ion channels.
- Forming recognition sites by identifying cells.
- Acting as carriers transporting water-soluble substances across the membrane.

The membrane as a barrier

Lipid-soluble substances move through the membrane via the phospholipid part. It prevents the entry or exit of water-soluble substances. The latter pass through special protein molecules, which form water-filled channels across the membrane. The cell surface membrane is selectively permeable to water and some solutes. Lipid-soluble substances can move through the cell membrane more easily than water-soluble substances.

- Small, uncharged molecules, such as oxygen and carbon dioxide, freely pass through the membrane as they are soluble in the lipid part.
- Lipid soluble molecules such as glycerol can pass through the membrane.
- The hydrophobic core of the membrane impedes the transport of ions and polar molecules.
- Charged particles (ions) and relatively large molecules such as glucose cannot diffuse across the non-polar centre of the phospholipid bilayer because they are relatively insoluble in lipid. Intrinsic proteins assist such particles to pass in or out of the cell by a passive process called facilitated diffusion.

Transport across cell membranes

Diffusion

Diffusion is the movement of molecules or ions from a region where they are in high concentration to a region of lower concentration until they are equally distributed. Ions and molecules are always in a state of random movement, but if they are highly concentrated in one area, there will be a net movement away from that area until equilibrium is reached or until there is a uniform distribution.

>> **Pointer**

The rate of diffusion is proportional to the difference in concentration between two areas. It is incorrect to state that it is proportional to concentration.

quickfire

㉑ State two features of the membrane that increase the rate of diffusion.

quickfire

㉒ Explain how an increase in temperature affects the rate of diffusion.

>> **Pointer**

Facilitated diffusion is a special form of diffusion that allows faster movement of molecules.

It is a passive process and occurs down a concentration gradient. However, it occurs at specific points on the plasma membrane where there are special protein molecules.

quickfire

㉓ How does facilitated diffusion differ from diffusion?

The rate of diffusion is affected by:

- The concentration gradient, i.e. the greater the difference in the concentration of molecules in two areas, the greater the rate.
- The distance of travel, i.e. the shorter the distance between two areas the greater the rate.
- The surface area of the membrane – the larger the area the quicker the rate.
- The thickness of the membrane – the thinner the membrane the greater the rate.
- An increase in temperature results in an increase in rate, since there is an increase in kinetic energy of molecules and therefore movement.

Facilitated diffusion

Charged particles or ions and large molecules such as glucose do not readily pass through the cell membrane because they are relatively insoluble in lipid. In the cell membrane, protein molecules span the membrane from one side to the other and help such particles to diffuse in to or out of the cells. These proteins are of two types:

- **Channel proteins** – consist of pores lined with polar groups allowing charged ions to pass through. (As the channel is hydrophilic, water-soluble substances can pass through.) As each channel protein is specific for one type of ion each protein will only let one particular ion through. They can also open and close according to the needs of the cell.
- **Carrier proteins** – allow the diffusion across the membrane of larger polar molecules such as sugars and amino acids. A particular molecule attaches to the carrier protein at its binding site and causes the carrier protein to change its shape, releasing the molecule through the membrane.

Carrier proteins and channel proteins increase the rate of diffusion along the concentration gradient without the need for energy in the form of ATP from respiration.

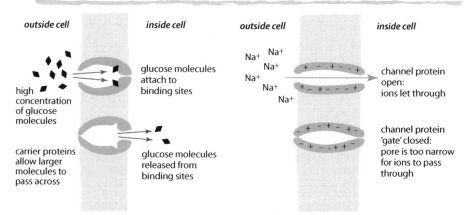

Carrier and channel proteins.

Active transport

Unlike the processes described so far, active transport is an energy-requiring process in which ions and molecules are moved across membranes against a concentration gradient.

The features of active transport are:

- Ions and molecules can move in the opposite direction to that in which diffusion occurs, i.e. against a concentration gradient.
- The energy for active transport is supplied by ATP, and anything which affects the respiratory process will affect active transport.
- Active transport will not take place in the presence of a respiratory inhibitor such as cyanide.
- The process occurs through the carrier proteins that span the membrane. The proteins accept the molecule and then the molecule enters the cell by a change in shape of the carrier molecule.

Processes involving active transport include protein synthesis, muscle contraction, nerve impulse transmission, absorption of mineral salts by plant roots.

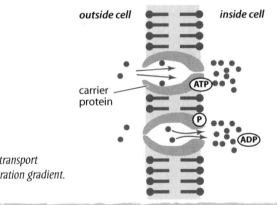

Carrier proteins use ATP to transport molecules against a concentration gradient.

» **Pointer**
The exchange of substances between cells and their surroundings occurs in ways that involve metabolic energy (active transport) and in ways that do not (passive transport).
  Passive processes require no external energy, only the kinetic energy of the molecules themselves.

24 State one similarity and one difference between facilitated diffusion and active transport.

25 Name two processes that involve active transport.

Graph showing effect of respiratory inhibitor on the rate of uptake of a substance across a cell membrane

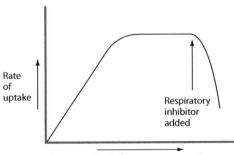

» **Pointer**
The graph shows that at higher concentration differences, a plateau is reached when the carrier proteins are saturated. The rate of uptake is affected with the addition of a respiratory inhibitor. Active transport must be taking place as the process needs ATP.

Solute = any substance that is dissolved in a solvent. Solutes and solvents form a solution.

Osmosis = the passage of water from a region of high water potential to a region of lower water potential through a partially permeable membrane.

≫ *Pointer*

Membranes are partially permeable, that is, they are permeable to water molecules and some other small molecules but not to larger molecules. Osmosis is a specialised form of diffusion involving only water molecules.

Grade boost

Water potential is the pressure created by water molecules and is measured in kilopascals (kPa). Pure water has a water potential of zero. The addition of a solute to pure water will lower the water potential. So the water potential of the solution has a negative value.

Grade boost

Be prepared to use the given equation in calculations.

quickfire

㉖ The water potential of three cells is:
Cell A = −150 kPa
Cell B = −200 kPa
Cell C = −100 kPa
Place the cells in the order that water would pass from one cell to the next.

Osmosis

Most cell membranes are permeable to water and certain **solutes** only. In biological systems **osmosis** is a special form of diffusion which involves the movement of water molecules only.

Biologists use the term water potential (WP) ψ(psi) to describe the tendency of water molecules to leave a system.

Pure water has the highest water potential of zero. This is because where there is a high concentration of water molecules, they have a greater potential energy, i.e. the water molecules are completely free to move about. When a solute, such as sugar, is dissolved in water, there are proportionally fewer water molecules to move about and the water potential of the solution is lowered. All water potentials (except that of pure water) have a negative value. The more concentrated the solution, the more negative the water potential, i.e. the fewer free water molecules there are.

In plant cells the following equation is used to describe the relationship between the forces:

$$\psi \quad = \quad \psi_s \quad + \quad \psi_p$$
water potential = solute potential + pressure potential

- The presence of solute molecules in the vacuole of a plant cell lowers the WP.
- The concentration of dissolved substances inside the cell vacuole determines the solute potential.
- When water enters a plant cell vacuole by osmosis, a hydrostatic pressure is set up and pushes outwards on the cell wall. As the outward pressure builds up, the cell wall develops an opposing force called the pressure potential. The pressure potential is usually positive.

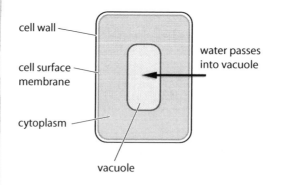
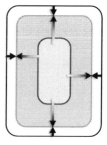

cell wall

cell surface membrane

cytoplasm

vacuole

water passes into vacuole

as water enters the cell, the rigid cell wall develops an opposing pressure potential

Solute and pressure potential.

Turgor and plasmolysis

- If the WP of the external solution is lower than that of the solution inside the cell, it is said to be hypertonic and water flows out of the cell.
- If the WP of the external solution is higher than that of the solution inside the cell, it is said to be hypotonic and water flows into the cell.
- If the cell has the same solute concentration as the surrounding solution, the external solution is isotonic with that of the cell.
- When a plant cell is placed in a hypertonic solution, it loses water by osmosis. The vacuole shrinks and the cytoplasm will draw away from the cell wall. This process is called plasmolysis and when complete, the cell is said to be flaccid.
- The point at which the cell membrane *just* begins to move away from the cell wall is said to be the point of incipient plasmolysis.
- A plant cell will gain water if placed in a hypotonic solution and will continue to take in water until prevented by the opposing pressure. The pressure potential rises until it is equal and opposite to the solute potential. In theory the water potential is now zero and when the cell cannot take in any more water it is said to be **turgid**. The state of turgor is important in plants, particularly young seedlings. It supports them and maintains their shape and form.

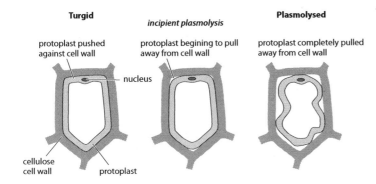

Turgid and plasmolysed cells.

As it has no cell wall, an animal cell is affected differently. If red blood cells are placed in distilled water, water enters by osmosis and they burst. This is called haemolysis. If red blood cells are placed into strong salt solution, water passes out of the cells and they shrink.

>> **Pointer**

In cells, metabolic reactions take place quickly and thousands of reactions are taking place simultaneously. Order and control are essential if reactions are not to interfere with each other. These features of metabolism are made possible by the action of enzymes.

>> **Pointer**

Induced fit model of enzyme action – this theory is a modified version of the lock and key hypothesis and proposes that the enzyme changes its shape slightly to accommodate the substrate. As the enzyme changes its shape it places a strain on the substrate molecule and distorts a particular bond. This lowers the activation energy needed to break the bond.

Grade boost

It is incorrect to state that the substrate has the 'same shape' as the active site. It has a complementary shape to the active site.

Enzymes

Enzyme structure

Enzymes are tertiary globular proteins where the protein chain is folded back on itself into a spherical or globular shape. Each enzyme has its own sequence of amino acids and is held in its tertiary form by hydrogen bonds, disulphide bridges and ionic bonds. This complex 3D shape gives the enzyme many of its properties. Although the enzyme molecule is large, only a small region, called the active site, is functional.

How enzymes work

Enzymes are biological catalysts that speed up the rate of metabolic reactions. These reactions can be of two types:

1. Reactions where larger molecules are broken down into smaller molecules.
2. Reactions where small molecules are built up into larger, more complex, molecules.

Enzymes react with another molecule called a substrate. Each enzyme has its own special shape, with an area, the active site, on to which the substrate molecules bind.

Enzyme + substrate $\longrightarrow$ enzyme-substrate complex $\longrightarrow$ enzyme + product.

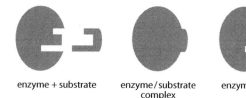

| enzyme + substrate | enzyme/substrate complex | enzyme + products |

Enzyme and substrate complex.

Properties of enzymes

- Enzymes are specific, i.e. each enzyme will catalyse only one particular reaction, for example sucrase acts on the sugar, sucrose.
- Enzymes are very efficient and have a high turnover number. This means that they can convert many molecules of substrate per unit time; for example, catalase, which breaks down the waste product hydrogen peroxide in the body, has a turnover number of several million!
- Chemical reactions need energy to start them off and this is called activation energy. This energy is needed to break the existing chemical bonds inside molecules. In the body, enzymes lower the activation energy of a reaction and so reduce the input of energy needed and allow reactions to take place at lower temperatures.

Factors affecting the rate of enzyme action

Enzymes are made inside living cells but may act inside the cell (intracellular) or outside (intercellular, extracellular) such as the digestive enzymes of the alimentary canal. Environmental conditions, such as temperature and pH, change the three-dimensional structure of enzyme molecules. Bonds are broken and hence the configuration of the active site is altered.

Grade boost

Enzymes are inactive at 0°C and if the temperature is raised they become active again. Enzymes are denatured at temperatures above 40°C.

Temperature

An increase in temperature gives molecules greater kinetic energy and they move around more quickly, increasing the chance of molecules colliding. Increasing the temperature of an enzyme-controlled reaction results in an increase in the rate of reaction. As a general rule, the rate of reaction doubles for each 10°C rise in temperature until an optimum temperature is reached. For most enzymes this is 40°C.

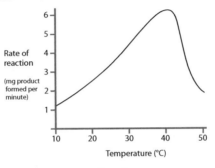

Graph showing effect of temperature on rate of reaction.

Above this temperature, the increasing vibration of the molecules causes the hydrogen bonds to break, causing a change in the tertiary structure of the enzyme. This alters the shape of the active site and the substrate will not fit into the active site. The enzyme is then said to be denatured. This is a permanent change in the structure. If enzymes are subjected to low temperatures, such as freezing, the enzyme is inactivated as the molecules have no kinetic energy. However, the enzyme can work again if the temperature is raised.

pH

The rate of an enzyme-catalysed reaction will vary with changes in pH. Enzymes have a narrow optimum range and small changes in pH can affect the rate of reaction without affecting the structure of the enzyme. Small changes in pH outside the optimum can cause small reversible changes in enzyme structure and result in inactivation. Extremes of pH can denature an enzyme.

The charges on the amino acid side-chains of the enzyme's active site are affected by free hydrogen ions or hydroxyl ions. In the formation of an enzyme–substrate complex the charge on the active site must match those on the substrate. If the active site has too many H^+ ions (say) the active site and the substrate may both have the same charge and the enzyme will repel the substrate.

quickfire

28 Describe the effect of an increase in temperature from 0°C to 40°C on the rate of an enzyme-controlled reaction.

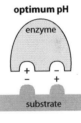

optimum pH

charges on active site match those of substrate so an enzyme–substrate complex forms

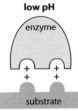

low pH

charges on active site repel substrate

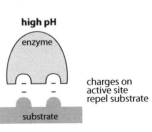

high pH

charges on active site repel substrate

Effect of pH.

≫ Pointer

Enzymes, rather than inorganic catalysts, are used widely in industry because they are more efficient. They have a higher turnover number and are very specific. They are also more economical as they work at lower temperatures.

≫ Pointer

Include all experimental work in your revision. There are often questions involving practical work in theory exams, particularly involving enzymes.

At extremes of pH the hydrogen bonding is affected and the three-dimensional shape of the enzyme is altered and so is the shape of the active site.

Enzymes are also affected by the concentration of the substrate and the concentration of the enzyme itself.

Substrate concentration

The rate of an enzyme-catalysed reaction will vary with changes in substrate concentration. If the amount of enzyme is constant, the rate of reaction will increase as the substrate increases. At low substrate concentrations the enzyme molecules have only a limited number of substrate molecules to collide with. In other words the active sites are not working to full capacity. As more substrate is added, there must come a point when all the enzyme's active sites are filled. In other words, the rate of reaction is at a maximum.

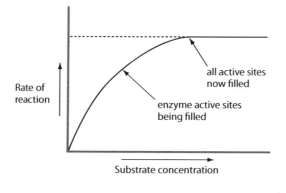

Graph showing effect of increasing substrate on rate of reaction.

Enzyme concentration

The rate of an enzyme-catalysed reaction will vary with changes in enzyme concentration. Increasing the enzyme concentration will increase the rate of reaction.

In enzyme experiments it is essential that buffers and controls are used:

- *Buffers* – buffers maintain a constant pH. When a buffer is used in an experiment, the pH changes little when a small quantity of acid or alkali is added. It may be said that a buffer 'soaks up hydrogen ions'.

- *Controls* – controls are duplicate experiments, identical in every respect to the actual experiment, except the variable being investigated, which is kept constant. For example, boiled and cooled enzyme may be used in a control experiment instead of the enzyme.

Enzyme inhibition

Inhibition occurs when enzyme action is slowed down or stopped by another substance. The inhibitor combines with the enzyme and either directly or indirectly prevents it forming an enzyme-substrate complex.

Competitive inhibition

The inhibitor is structurally similar to the substrate and competes with the active site of the enzyme, i.e. the inhibitor has a shape that lets it fit into the active site of the enzyme in place of the substrate. For example, malonic acid competes with succinate for the active sites of succinic dehydrogenase, an important enzyme in the Krebs cycle in respiration. If the substrate concentration is increased, it will reduce the effect of the inhibitor. This is because the more substrate molecules present, the greater the chance of finding active sites, leaving fewer to be occupied by the inhibitor.

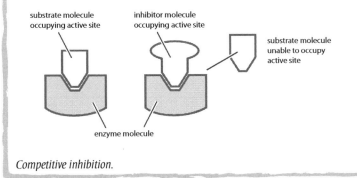

Competitive inhibition.

Non-competitive inhibition

The inhibitor binds to the enzyme at a site away from the active site. This alters the overall shape of the enzyme molecule, including the active site, in such a way that the active site can no longer accommodate the substrate. As the substrate and inhibitor molecules attach to different parts of the enzyme, they are not competing for the same sites. The rate of reaction is therefore unaffected by substrate concentration. For example, cyanide (a respiratory poison) attaches itself to part of the enzyme cytochrome oxidase, and inhibits respiration.

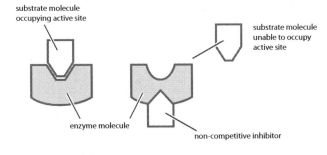

Non-competitive inhibition.

Grade boost

Describe enzyme–substrate reactions in terms of molecular collisions. With competitive inhibition the greater the substrate concentration compared with the inhibitor, the greater the chance that the substrate will collide with the enzyme.

quickfire

㉛ State how the two types of inhibitors differ in how they attach to an enzyme.

quickfire

㉜ In an experiment an enzyme-controlled reaction is inhibited by substance A. Suggest the experimental change which could be made to determine whether the inhibitor is competitive or non-competitive.

Grade boost

Do not be too concerned with the functions of malonic acid and cytochrome oxidase at this stage. These chemicals and their involvement in respiration may be studied at A2.

Medical and industrial applications of enzymes

Immobilised enzymes

These are enzyme molecules that are fixed, bound or trapped on an inert matrix such as a gel capsule (alginate beads). These beads can be packed into glass columns. Substrate can be added to the top of the column and it reacts with the enzyme as it slowly flows down the column. Once set up, the column can be used again

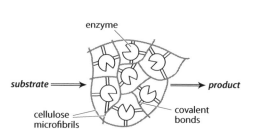

Immobilised enzymes in a framework of cellulose microfibrils.

and again. As the enzyme is fixed it does not get mixed up with the products and is therefore cheaper to separate. Immobilised enzymes are used widely in industrial processes, such as fermentation, as they can readily be recovered for reuse.

Enzyme instability is one of the key factors that prevent the wider use of 'free' enzymes. Chemicals such as organic solvents, raised temperatures and pH values outside the norm can denature the enzyme with a consequent loss of activity. Immobilising enzymes with a polymer matrix creates a microenvironment allowing reactions to occur at higher temperatures than normal. This means that activity is increased and so production is also increased.

Other advantages include:

- Enzymes can tolerate a wider range of conditions.
- Enzymes are easily recovered for reuse thus reducing overall costs.
- Several enzymes with differing pH or temperature optima can be used together.
- Enzymes can be easily added or removed giving greater control over the reaction.

Grade boost

You should be able to list the advantages of immobilised enzymes.

quickfire

㉝ Using the graph, list three differences between the effects of temperature on the immobilised and free enzyme.

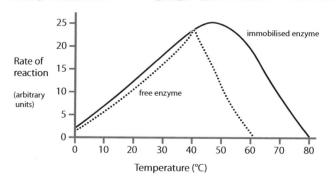

Graph showing effect of temperature on free and immobilised enzymes.

Biosensors

One use of immobilised enzymes involves **biosensors**, which work on the principle that enzymes are specific and are able to select one type of molecule from a mixture even in very low concentrations. A biosensor can be used in the rapid and accurate detection of minute traces of biologically important molecules.

Biosensors have great potential in the areas of medical diagnosis and environmental monitoring. The electrode probe can detect changes in substrate or product, temperature changes or optical properties.

One particular use of a biosensor is in the detection of blood sugar in diabetics. The electrode probe, which has a specific enzyme immobilised in a membrane, is placed in the blood sample. If glucose is present, it diffuses through the membrane, and forms an enzyme-substrate complex. The reaction produces a small electric current, which is picked up by the electrode (the transducer). This current is read by a meter which produces a reading for blood glucose. Normal blood glucose levels are described as being 3.89–5.83 mmol dm^{-3}.

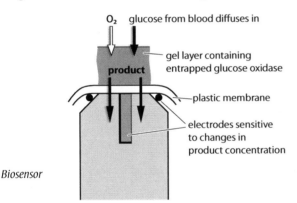

Biosensor

Steps in using a biosensor:

1. Blood contains a mixture of different molecules.
2. Enzyme electrode is placed in a blood sample.
3. Glucose diffuses into the immobilised enzyme layer.
4. Oxygen is taken up.
5. The rate of oxygen uptake is proportional to the glucose concentration.
6. A digital display shows an accurate concentration of glucose.

Key Term

Biosensor = describes the association of a biomolecule, such as an enzyme, with a transducer, which produces an electrical signal in response to substrate transformation. The strength of the electrical signal may be measured with a meter.

≫ Pointer

Immobilised enzymes are also used in pregnancy testing kits and in a fermenter to provide a rapid, sensitive and specific measurement of products.

quickfire

(34) The Benedict's test is at best semi-quantitative estimating the approximate concentration of glucose in a sample. State two advantages of using a biosensor.

>> *Pointer*

DNA performs two major functions:

- Replication in dividing cells.
- Carrying the information for protein synthesis.

These processes are included in the A2 specification.

>> *Pointer*

DNA determines inherited characteristics and contains information in the form of the genetic code.

>> *Pointer*

Bases that pair together are called complementary base pairs. A pairs with T, and C pairs with G. In an exam answer do not use abbreviations!

>> *Pointer*

Nitrogenous bases derived from pyrimidines are single ring structures, whereas those derived from purines are double ring structures.

Grade boost

Cytosine and thymine include the letter 'Y', so does pyrimidine!

Nucleic acids

There are two types of nucleic acid: deoxyribonucleic acid (DNA) and ribonucleic acid (RNA). Both are built up of units called nucleotides. Individual nucleotides are made up of three parts that combine by condensation reactions. These are:

- Phosphate ion. This has the same structure in all nucleotides.
- Pentose sugar, of which there are two types:
  1. In ribonucleic acid (RNA) the sugar is ribose.
  2. In deoxyribonucleic acid (DNA) the sugar is deoxyribose.
- Organic base which contains nitrogen.

There are five different bases which are divided into two groups:

- The pyrimidine bases (single ring structures) are thymine, cytosine and uracil.
- The purine bases (double ring structures) are adenine and guanine.

The structure of DNA

- DNA is a double-stranded **polymer** of nucleotides or polynucleotide.
- Each polynucleotide may contain many million nucleotide units.
- It is in the form of a double helix, the shape of which is maintained by hydrogen bonding.
- The pentose sugar is always deoxyribose.
- DNA contains four organic bases. These are adenine, guanine, cytosine, and thymine.
- Each strand is linked to the other by pairs of organic bases.
- Cytosine always pairs with guanine, adenine always pairs with thymine, and the bases are joined by hydrogen bonds.
- Put simply, DNA is like a coiled ladder with the uprights of the ladder being made up of alternating sugars and phosphate groups and the rungs made up of the bases. The bases are held together by weak hydrogen bonds.

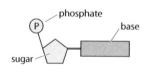

Nucleotide

Part of a DNA chain showing a polynucleotide consisting of three base pairs.

How DNA is well suited to carry out its functions:

- It is a very stable molecule and can pass from generation to generation without change.
- It is a very large molecule and can carry a large amount of genetic information.
- The two strands are able to separate easily as they are held together by weak hydrogen bonds.
- As the base pairs are held within the deoxyribose-phosphate backbone, the genetic information is protected from outside forces.

Grade boost
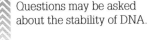

Questions may be asked about the stability of DNA.

Pointer
At AS you are not required to have a knowledge of protein synthesis.

The structure of RNA

- RNA is a single-stranded polymer of nucleotide.
- RNA contains the pentose sugar, ribose.
- RNA contains the organic bases adenine, guanine, cytosine, and uracil (in place of thymine).

There are three types of RNA and all are involved in the process of protein synthesis:

- Messenger RNA (mRNA) is a long single-stranded molecule formed into a helix. It is manufactured in the nucleus and carries the genetic code from the DNA to the ribosomes in the cytoplasm.
- Ribosomal RNA (rRNA) is found in the cytoplasm and is a large, complex molecule made up of both double and single helices. Ribosomes are made up of ribosomal RNA and protein. They are the site of translation of the genetic code.
- Transfer RNA (tRNA) is a small single-stranded molecule. It forms a clover-leaf shape, with one end of the chain ending in a cytosine-cytosine-adenine sequence at which point the amino acid it carries attaches itself. At the opposite end of the chain is a sequence of three bases called the anticodon. tRNA molecules transport amino acids to the ribosome so that proteins can be synthesised.

Comparing DNA and RNA

	DNA	RNA
Sugar	Deoxyribose	Ribose
Bases	CGAT	CGAU
Helix	Double	Single

 **quickfire**

㉟ State which type of RNA is found in the cytoplasm only and which type can be found in the nucleus and cytoplasm.

quickfire

㊱ State two differences between DNA and RNA.

Grade boost

» Pointer

The number of chromosomes in the cells of different species varies. Humans always have 46 chromosomes, a fruit fly has 8 chromosomes, a potato 48 chromosomes! Chromosomes are found in matching pairs, called homologous pairs. So humans have 23 pairs of homologous chromosomes. The total number of chromosomes is called the diploid number. Sex cells, or gametes, have half the diploid number, this is called haploid. Human gametes have 23 chromosomes.

Cell division

Genetic information is copied and passed on to daughter cells.

Chromosome structure

Chromosomes are made up of DNA, protein and a small amount of RNA. DNA occurs as a single strand in the form of a double helix running the length of the chromosome. Each DNA molecule is made up of many sections called genes. It is only at the onset of cell division that chromosomes become visible. Shortly before cell division begins, each DNA molecule makes a copy of itself. The single thread of DNA becomes two identical threads. These are called chromatids and they lie parallel along most of their length but are joined only in a specialised region called the centromere.

Mitosis

Mitosis produces two daughter cells that are genetically identical to the parent cell.

Dividing cells undergo a regular pattern of events known as the cell cycle. This is a continuous process but for convenience of description it is subdivided into four stages preceded by a period when the cell is not dividing. This is called interphase and is the longest part of the cycle.

During interphase a newly formed cell increases in size and produces organelles lost during the previous division. The amount of DNA is also doubled. Just before the next cell division the chromosomes replicate so that each then consists of two chromatids joined together by the centromere. There is considerable metabolic activity as these processes need energy in the form of ATP. The chromosomes are not visible at interphase because the chromosome material, chromatin, is dispersed throughout the nucleus.

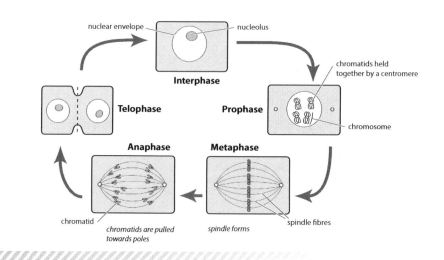

Stages in mitosis.

Stages in mitosis

Prophase – The chromosomes condense (shorten and become thicker) and become visible as long thin threads. They are now referred to as pairs of chromatids. In cells where centrioles are present, i.e. animals and lower plants, the centrioles replicate and move to the opposite ends (poles) of the cells. Protein microtubules form from each centriole and the spindle develops, extending from pole to pole. Towards the end of prophase the nuclear membrane disintegrates and the nucleolus disappears. Pairs of chromatids can clearly be seen lying free in the cytoplasm.

Metaphase –The chromosomes arrange themselves at the centre or equator of the spindle and become attached to certain spindle fibres at the centromere. Contraction of these fibres draws the individual chromatids slightly apart.

Anaphase – A very rapid stage. The centromere splits and the spindle fibres contract and pull the now separated chromatids to the poles, centromere first.

Telophase –The chromosomes have now reached the poles of the cells and are referred to as chromosomes again. They uncoil and lengthen. The spindle breaks down, the nucleoli reappear and the nuclear membrane reforms. In animal cells cytokinesis occurs by the constriction of the centre of the parent cell from the outside inwards. In plant cells, a cell plate forms across the equator of the parent cell from the centre outwards and a new cell wall is laid down.

Significance of mitosis

- Mitosis produces two cells that have the same number of chromosomes as the parent cell and each chromosome is an exact replica of one of the originals. The division allows the production of cells that are genetically identical to the parent and so gives genetic stability.

- By producing new cells, mitosis leads to growth of an organism and also allows for repair of tissues and the replacement of dead cells. An example of mitosis in plants is in the root tip. In human skin, dead surface cells are replaced by identical cells from below.

- Asexual reproduction results in complete offspring that are identical to the parent. This takes place in unicellular organisms such as yeast and bacteria. It also takes place in certain flowering plants where organs such as bulbs, tubers and runners produce large numbers of identical offspring in a relatively short period of time. There is no variation between individuals. However, most of these plants also reproduce sexually.

quickfire

(37) Interphase is a period of intense metabolic activity. State three events that occur during this stage.

Grade boost

Mitosis is a continuous process. Under the microscope you will see only a snapshot of what is happening.

Grade boost

Be prepared to recognise the stages of mitosis from drawings and photographs and explain the events occurring during each stage. You may also be required to draw and label a particular stage.

quickfire

(38) With particular reference to plants, what is the significance of mitosis?

Key Term

Homologous = in the diploid cell each chromosome has a partner of exactly the same length and with precisely the same genes.

≫ Pointer

You are not required to describe the complete process of meiosis but to describe the significance of the differences between mitosis and meiosis.

Meiosis

In sexual reproduction two gametes fuse to form a zygote. For each generation to maintain a full set of chromosomes (diploid number) the chromosome number must be halved (haploid number) during meiosis. Meiosis involves two divisions: meiosis I where the chromosome number is halved, and meiosis II where the two haploid nuclei divide again in a division identical to that of mitosis. The end result is the production of four daughter nuclei, each with half the number of chromosomes of the parent cell.

However, there is another important difference between meiosis and mitosis. During prophase I homologous chromatids wrap around each other and then partially repel each other but remain joined at certain points called chiasmata. At these points chromatids may break and recombine with a different but equivalent chromatid. This swapping of pieces of chromosomes is called crossing over and is a source of genetic variation.

During the first stage of metaphase of meiosis the pairs of **homologous** chromosomes arrange themselves randomly on the equator of the spindle. Only one of each pair passes into the daughter cell and this happens with each pair. Therefore the combination of chromosomes that goes into the daughter cell at meiosis I is also random. This random distribution and consequent independent assortment of chromosomes produces new genetic combinations.

Comparison of mitosis and meiosis

Mitosis	Meiosis
One division resulting in two daughter cells	Two divisions resulting in four daughter cells
Number of chromosomes is unchanged	Number of chromosomes is halved
Homologous chromosomes do not associate in pairs	Homologous chromosomes pair up
Crossing over does not occur	Crossing over occurs and chiasmata form
Daughter cells are genetically identical	Daughter cells are genetically different

Meiosis and variation

㊴ State three differences between meiosis and mitosis.

㊵ Explain how meiosis can give rise to genetically variable gametes.

In the long term, if a species is to survive in a constantly changing environment and to colonise new environments, sources of variation are essential. There are three ways of creating variety:

- During sexual reproduction the genotype of one parent is mixed with that of the other when haploid gametes fuse.
- Independent assortment results in gametes containing different combinations of chromosomes.
- During crossing over equivalent parts of homologous chromosomes may be exchanged thus producing new combinations and the separation of linked genes.

Summary: Basic Biochemistry and Cell Structure

Basic biochemistry

Chemical properties of carbohydrates, fats and proteins related to chemical structure

Carbohydrates

A source of energy, polymers add strength and support

Lipids

Energy stores, insulation and protection, and component of cell membrane

Proteins

Enzymes, hormones, antibodies, transport and structural

Water is an important solvent and is involved in biochemical reactions

DNA

- Double helix with base pairs bonded together
- Deoxyribose sugar
- Sequence of bases called the genetic code
- Replicates during cell division
- RNA differs from DNA

Cell structure

Prokaryotes

Simple organisms such as bacteria with no membrane-bound organelles

Eukaryotes

- Plants, animals, fungi and protoctists with membrane-bound organelles
- Variety of organelles

Cell membrane

- Consists of phospholipids and proteins
- Fluid Mosaic model
- Transport of materials by diffusion, facilitated diffusion, active transport and osmosis

Enzymes

- Globular proteins
- Properties related to tertiary structure
- Combine with a substrate to form an enzyme-substrate complex
- Affected by factors such as temperature, pH, and the concentration of the reactants
- Inhibited by competitive and non-competitive inhibitors
- Used widely in industry in immobilised form

Cell division

Mitosis

- Asexual reproduction and growth and repair of cells
- Daughter cells genetically identical to the parent

Meiosis

- Haploid gametes produced
- Daughter cells genetically different

Biochemistry

1. The following diagrams represent the structure of four biologically important compounds.

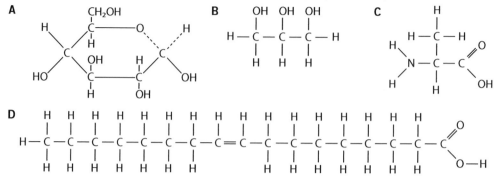

(a) A chemical element found in a molecule of compound **C** is not found in molecules of the other three compounds. Name this element. (1)

(b) A reducing sugar in solution can be detected in the laboratory.

 (i) Describe the biochemical test you would use to show that the solution contained a reducing sugar. (2)

 (ii) Which of the compounds **A** to **D** will give a positive result with this biochemical test? (1)

(c) Which of the compounds **A** to **D** has molecules that will join together by peptide bonds? (1)

(d) (i) Which of the compounds **A** to **D** is a fatty acid? (1)

 (ii) State how the structure of a saturated fatty acid differs from the structure of an unsaturated fatty acid. (2)

WJEC BY1 JUNE 2012

2. The diagram represents part of a cellulose molecule.

(a) (i) Name bond Z as shown on the diagram. (1)

 (ii) Explain the importance of bond Z in the role of cellulose in plant cell walls. (2)

(b) (i) Name the chemical reaction in which molecules of this monomer join together to form cellulose. (1)

 (ii) Chitin has many chemical and structural similarities to cellulose.
 In chitin what additional compound replaces one of the −OH groups in each of its monosaccharides? (1)

 (iii) State the structural role of chitin in insects and describe the properties that make it suitable for this role. (1)

(c) Other polysaccharides have a storage function. Name a storage polysaccharide found in:

 (i) animal cells (1) (ii) plant cells (1)

WJEC BY1 JAN 2012

3. Below is a list of chemicals which may be found in cells.

A magnesium D cellulose G phosphate
B maltose E iron H water
C amino acid F calcium I sucrose

Each of the following statements applies to one or more of these chemicals.

Identify the letter or letters which correspond(s) to the chemical(s) being described. Each letter may be used once, more than once, or not at all. (6)

(a) A large quantity of energy is needed to raise its temperature.

(b) Found in bones and teeth.

(c) A non-reducing sugar.

(d) Found in chlorophyll in leaves.

(e) A polysaccharide found in plant cell walls.

(f) Found attached to lipids in the plasma membrane.

WJEC BY1 JAN 2009

Cell structure and organisation

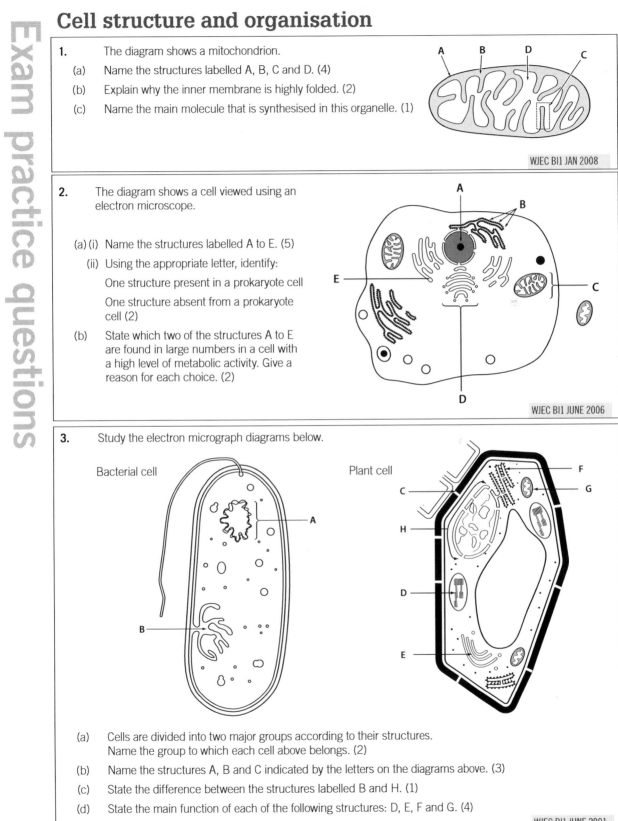

1. The diagram shows a mitochondrion.

(a) Name the structures labelled A, B, C and D. (4)

(b) Explain why the inner membrane is highly folded. (2)

(c) Name the main molecule that is synthesised in this organelle. (1)

WJEC BI1 JAN 2008

2. The diagram shows a cell viewed using an electron microscope.

(a) (i) Name the structures labelled A to E. (5)

(ii) Using the appropriate letter, identify:

One structure present in a prokaryote cell

One structure absent from a prokaryote cell (2)

(b) State which two of the structures A to E are found in large numbers in a cell with a high level of metabolic activity. Give a reason for each choice. (2)

WJEC BI1 JUNE 2006

3. Study the electron micrograph diagrams below.

Bacterial cell

Plant cell

(a) Cells are divided into two major groups according to their structures. Name the group to which each cell above belongs. (2)

(b) Name the structures A, B and C indicated by the letters on the diagrams above. (3)

(c) State the difference between the structures labelled B and H. (1)

(d) State the main function of each of the following structures: D, E, F and G. (4)

WJEC BI1 JUNE 2001

Membranes and transport

1. The diagram below shows two adjacent plant cells, placed in a 0.6 molar glucose solution.

(a) Name the parts labelled A–F. (3)

(b) State two ways by which materials move between cell X and cell Y. (2)

(c) Cells X and Y are at incipient plasmolysis, in a 0.6 molar glucose solution. Describe one change that would be visible under the microscope, if the cells were placed in a 1.0 molar glucose solution. (1)

(d) The water potential of vacuolated cells is represented by the equation:

$$\psi \text{ cell} = \psi_s + \psi_p$$

(i) Define the term 'water potential'. (1)

(ii) State the value of ψ_p in cells at incipient plasmolysis. (1)

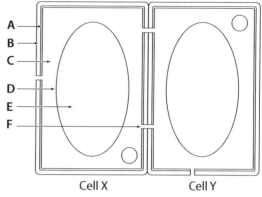

(iii) Two different cells P and Q are adjacent to one another in a plant. Calculate the missing values for each cell and complete the table. (2)

Cell	ψ cell kPa	ψ_s kPa	ψ_p kPa
P	-------	−1200	+500
Q	−300	--------	+300

(iv) In which direction will water move between these two cells? (1)

WJEC BY1 JUNE 2009

2. The diagram shows the plasma membrane of an animal cell.

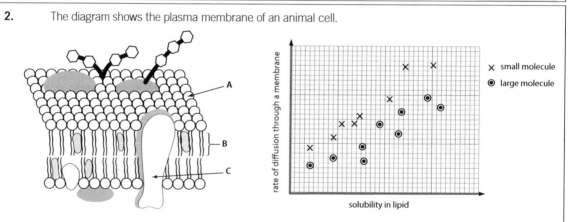

(a) State the names of the structures labelled A, B and C. (3)

(b) The graph shows the effect of molecule size and solubility in lipid on the rate of diffusion of substances through a cell surface membrane.

(i) State with an explanation how the solubility in lipid affects the rate of diffusion through a membrane. (2)

(ii) Describe how molecular size affects the rate of diffusion.

Suggest an explanation for your answer. (2)

(c) Name two factors which affect the rate of facilitated diffusion of a substance through a membrane. (2)

(d) Vitamins B1 and K enter cells by crossing the plasma membrane. As vitamin B1 is water soluble while vitamin K is fat soluble they take different routes across the membrane.

Explain how the different routes taken by these vitamins into a cell are determined by the structure of the plasma membrane. (4)

WJEC BY1 JAN 2012

Enzymes

1. The graph represents the effect of an increase in temperature on the rate of enzyme activity.

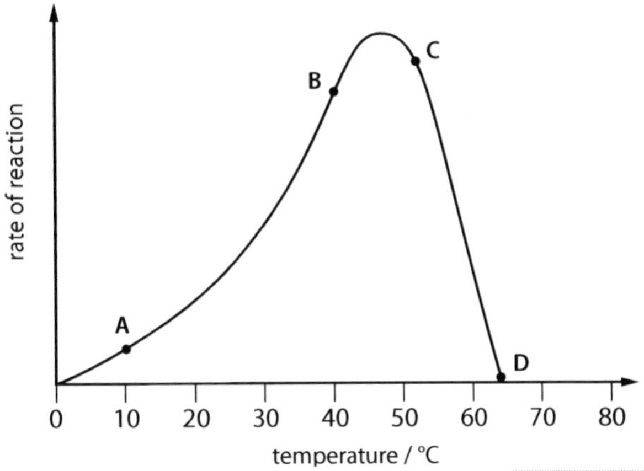

(a) Give an explanation for the shape of the curve between:

(i) A and B

(ii) C and D. (4)

(b) Suggest why the temperature of a mammal is maintained just below the optimum temperature for the enzymes in that mammal. (2)

WJEC BI1 JUNE 2004

2. (a) Diagrams A and B represent two different types of enzyme inhibition.

(i) State the type of inhibition shown in A and B. (2)

(ii) What type of inhibition A or B would be decreased by increasing the concentration of substrate? (1)

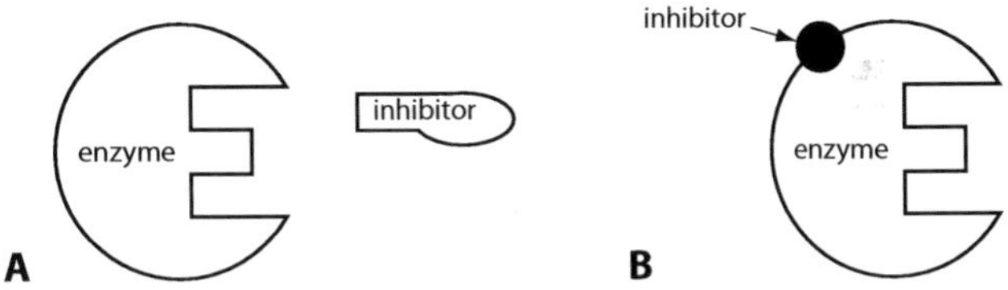

(b) Immobilised enzymes are enzyme molecules that are trapped on an inert matrix such as a gel capsule.

The graph shows the effect of temperature on the maximum rate of reaction of the **same** enzyme in its free and in its immobilised state.

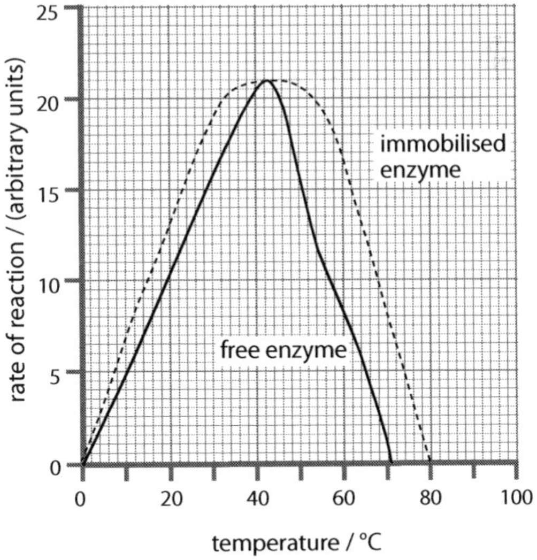

(i) Explain the rate of reaction at 5°C and 70°C for the **free** enzyme. (2)

(ii) Describe three differences between the effects of temperature on the immobilised and the 'free' enzyme. (3)

(iii) Suggest how trapping the enzyme in an inert matrix can explain the differences you have described in part (b)(ii). (1)

(iv) State one use of immobilised enzymes in medicine. (1)

WJEC BY1 JAN 2009

Nucleic acids

1. The DNA molecule is a double helix. It may be described as a coiled ladder.

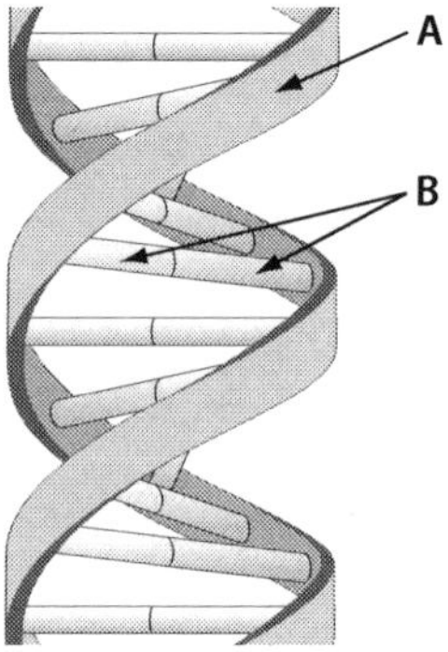

    (a) What are the 'uprights' of the ladder, labelled A, made of? (1)

    (b) The 'rungs' are made by pairing the components labelled B.

        Name the components in their complementary pairs. (2)

    (c) Name the type of bonds that hold the pairs together. (1)

WJEC BY1 JUNE 2009

2. The diagram represents the molecular structure of part of a DNA molecule.

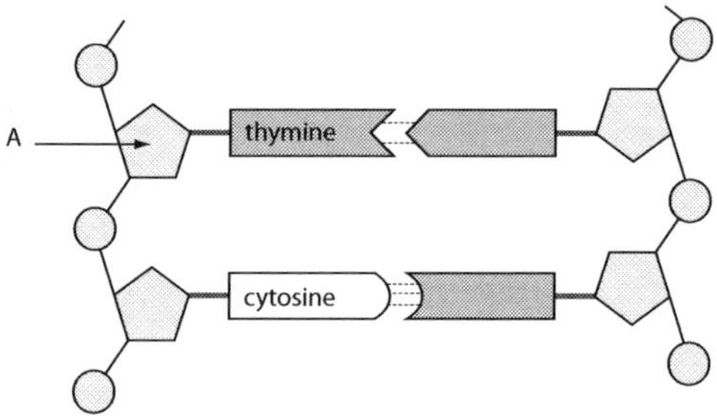

    (a) Name part A. (1)

    (b) Part of a DNA molecule has the following sequence of bases.

        T-A-T-C-G

    (i) In the table below write the letters for the sequence of bases of the complementary portion of DNA. (1)

DNA molecule	T	A	T	C	G
complementary DNA					

    (ii) Biochemical analysis of a sample of DNA showed that 30% of the bases were guanine. Calculate the percentage of the bases in the sample which would be adenine. (2)

WJEC BY1 JAN 2012

3. The diagrams represent two biological molecules.

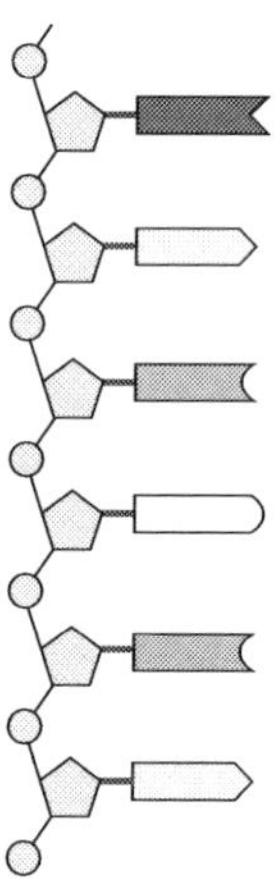

    (a) Name molecules A and B. (1)

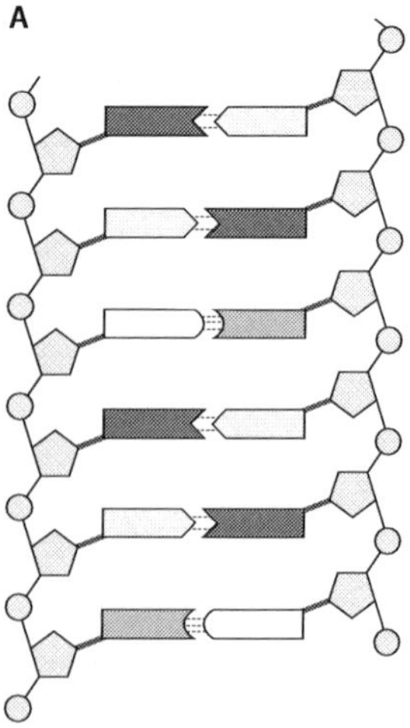

    (b) Where in the cell would you find molecule A? (1)

    (c) Name the bond which holds the two strands together in A. (1)

    (d) State one other structural difference, not shown in the diagram, between the two molecules A and B. (1)

WJEC BI1 JUNE 2005

Cell division

1. The diagram shows a stage in cell division.

(a) Name structures A, B, C and D. (4)

(b) Name the phase shown in the diagram. (1)

(c) (i) Name the type of division shown. (1)

   (ii) Give one reason for your answer to (c)(i) (1)

(d) State one biological function of this type of division. (1)

(e) The diagram shows an early stage in this phase.
A diagram drawn at the end of this phase would show
several changes. State three of these changes. (3)

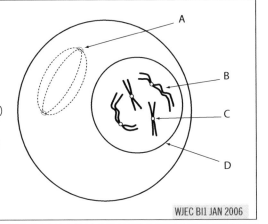

WJEC BI1 JAN 2006

2. Name the stage of mitosis where each of the following occurs. (5)

(a) Chromatids line up at the equator.

(b) Centromeres split.

(c) Spindle fibres contract and shorten.

(d) Chromosomes are first visible as pairs of chromatids.

(e) Nuclear membrane reforms.

WJEC BY1 JAN 2010

3. (a) The diagram represents the events that take place during the cell cycle.

The table below shows the DNA content of a cell measured during one cell cycle.

Stage	DNA content of cell/arbitrary units
G1	20
S	20 increasing to 40
G2	40
M	40
C	40 decreasing to 20

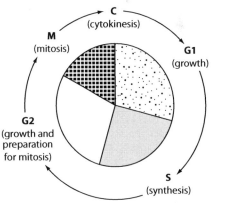

  (i) State the name of the period in the cell cycle that
includes stages G1, S and G2. (1)

  (ii) Apart from changes in DNA content, state two other events that occur during this period. (2)

(b) Using information provided in the diagram and the table explain why it is important that the DNA content
of the cell increases during stage S and decreases during stage C. (2)

(c) Explain how mitosis maintains genetic stability. (2)

WJEC BY1 JAN 2012

HB2: Biodiversity and Physiology of Body Systems

This unit gives an overview of the variety of organisms with an emphasis on human physiology. Evolution has brought about the existence of the biodiversity of life-forms on Earth. Human evolution is a controversial subject and elaborate theories have been proposed in an attempt to explain how humans evolved. The structure and function of selected human systems is studied. These include the digestive system, respiratory system and the circulatory system. There is an emphasis on conditions affecting the human body and the importance of maintaining a healthy lifestyle. The human body also acts as a host to a number of other living organisms that are harmful and cause disease. Selected examples of these diseases are studied together with the various defence mechanisms that operate to defend against and rid the body of disease.

Revision checklist

Tick column 1 when you have completed brief revision notes.
Tick column 2 when you think you have a good grasp of the topic.
Tick column 3 during final revision when you feel you have mastery of the topic.

		1	2	3	Notes
p46	**Biodiversity and evolution**				
p47	Evolution				
p48	Classification				
p50	Human evolution				
p55	Evidence of common ancestry				
	Uptake of energy and nutrients				
p56	Processing food in the digestive system				
p57	Structure of the human gut				
p58	Digestion				
p61	Absorption				
p62	Conditions affecting the digestive system				
	Gas exchange				
p65	Problems associated with increase in size				
p66	The human respiratory system				
p69	Respiratory disease				
p70	Effects of smoking				

Revision checklist

		1	2	3	Notes
	Transport to and from exchange surfaces				
p72	Structure and functions of blood				
p73	Blood groups				
p74	Anaemia				
p75	The circulatory system				
p80	Monitoring circulation				
p84	Treatment of heart disease				
p85	The transport of gases				
p88	Intercellular fluid				
	Human defence mechanisms				
p90	Non-specific mechanisms				
p92	Specific mechanisms				
p95	Types of immunity				
p96	Vaccination				
	Pathogens, the spread of human disease and the control of infection				
p99	Disease transmission				
p100	Control and treatment of selected diseases				
p104	Antibiotics				
p107	Parasitism				

Biodiversity and evolution

Grade boost

Research an ecosystem currently under threat due to human activity.
For a named endangered species in that ecosystem list the factors that have led to its endangered status. Consider the steps being made to conserve the species.

quickpire

① State the two main causes for the decline in the numbers of tigers.

Pointer

Evolutionary history shows that biodiversity has gone through several bottlenecks called mass extinctions followed by radiations of new species.

Human activities are altering ecosystems upon which they and other species depend. Tropical rain forests are being destroyed at an alarming rate to make room for, and to support, the increase in the human population. In the oceans, stocks of many fishes are being depleted by over-harvesting, and some of the most productive and diverse areas, such as coral reefs and estuaries, are being severely stressed. Globally, the rate of species loss may be as much as 50 times higher than at any time in the past 100,000 years. Human alteration to habitat is the single greatest threat to **biodiversity** on the planet.

Extinction is a natural process that has been taking place since life first evolved. It is the current *rate* of extinction that underlies the biodiversity crisis. Scientists believe that the normal 'background' rate of extinction is one out of every million species per year. It is now estimated that human activity in tropical areas alone has increased extinction rates between 1000 and 10,000 times! Massive destruction of habitats throughout the world has been brought about by agriculture, urban development, forestry, mining, and environmental pollution. Marine life has also been affected. About one third of the planet's marine fish species rely on coral reefs. At the current rate of destruction about half of the reefs could be lost in the next 20 years.

The vast majority of Earth's earlier occupants, including the large and once dominant dinosaurs and tree ferns, have become extinct largely as a result of climatic, geological and biotic changes. At the present time, human activity has taken over as the main cause of species **evolution**. The decline in numbers of larger mammals such as mountain gorillas, giant pandas, tigers and polar bears is mainly due to loss of habitat, over-hunting by humans and competition from introduced species. Other species are also threatened by additional causes such as deforestation, pollution and drainage of wetlands.

It is now recognised that each species may represent an important human asset, a potential source of food, useful chemicals, or disease-resistant genes. Of the many plants growing in the tropical rain forests there may be some with medicinal properties. The extinction of any plant species before its chemical properties have been investigated could amount to an incalculable loss. There is therefore a need for species conservation, the planned preservation of wildlife.

Evolution

What has brought about the existence of so many different life-forms on Earth? The term evolution is used specifically for the processes that have transformed life on Earth from its early beginnings to the vast diversity of fossilised and living forms that are known today.

The theory of evolution was first proposed by Charles Darwin.

Darwin studied the fourteen different species of finches found on the Galapagos Islands. Finches are unable to fly long distances and, since the mainland is 600 miles distant, Darwin suggested that one ancestral species of finch had reached the islands with the help of the prevailing winds. As there were no other bird species inhabiting the islands, there was a variety of food available to the colonising finches. He noticed how individual finches differed from one island to the next. The main differences were in the size and shape of their beaks and these were related to the different type of food eaten, for example insects, seeds, fruit.

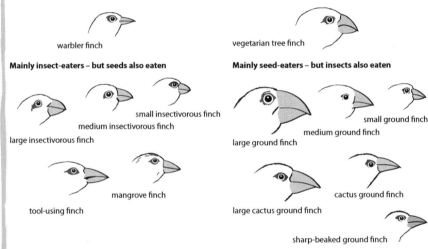

Different types of finch beaks.

It seemed that on each island the characteristics that best suited a particular finch to its environment were inherited by the offspring. Darwin suggested that the finches had developed from a common ancestor and that the type of beak had developed over time and become specialised to feed on a particular food source. This is an example of **adaptive radiation.**

Key Term

Adaptive radiation = the emergence of several new species from a common ancestor introduced into an environment.

Grade boost

Evolution and natural selection drive the development of new species.

>> Pointer

You are not required to study Darwin's theory of natural selection.

>> Pointer

In 1832, Charles Darwin studied the flora and fauna of mainland South America and of some surrounding islands, including the Galapagos Islands. These islands were formed in recent geological time, the result of volcanic activity. His task was to observe, describe and classify the plants and animals that he found. He also collected fossils in the rocks and these showed him that different life-forms had gone through many changes in the past. In 1859 he proposed natural selection as the force that causes changes in populations.

Key Terms

Taxonomy = the scientific study of the diversity of living organisms.

Taxon = a level in the classification hierarchy consisting of a collection of organisms sharing some basic features.

Species = a group of similar organisms that can breed together to produce fertile offspring.

Grade boost

You should know about the principles of modern classification that show how organisms may be related through evolution by the number of common characteristics they share.

Grade boost

Be prepared to place taxa in the correct order.

quickfire

② What is the definition of a species?

Grade boost

Note that the genus name is given a capital letter and the species name is in lower case. Both are in italics, or, if hand-written, underlined.

》 Pointer

You are required to know only the names of each taxon from kingdom through to species. The named examples given are for illustration only.

Classification

It is believed that there are between 3 and 30 million species of living organisms on Earth but, to date, only about two million different kinds of organisms have been described and identified. The sorting of living organisms into groups of a manageable size is known as **taxonomy** or classification.

When describing plants and animals taxonomists look for differences and similarities between them and place similar organisms closely together and dissimilar ones further apart. A classification system based on large groups being divided up into progressively smaller groups is said to be hierarchical.

The natural classification used today was devised by Swedish scientist, Linnaeus, in the 18th century. In this scheme organisms are grouped together according to their basic similarities. A hierarchical system has been devised to distinguish large groups of organisms with a series of rank names to identify the different levels within the hierarchy. Each level in this classification hierarchy is called a **taxon**.

- Kingdom – the largest taxonomic grouping, e.g. animals, plants.
- Phylum – a large grouping of all the classes that share some common features, e.g. Arthropods (includes insects, spiders, centipedes and millipedes, crustaceans).
- Class – a grouping of similar orders, e.g. Insecta (insects).
- Order – grouping of related families, e.g. Orthoptera (includes locusts, grasshoppers and crickets).
- Family – a grouping of similar genera (plural of genus), e.g. Locustidae
- Genus – a group of species that are very closely related, for example *Locusta*.
- Species – a group of organisms which share a large number of common characteristics and which can interbreed to produce fertile offspring, for example *Locusta migratoria*.

Moving up the hierarchy from **species** to kingdom means that the relationship between organisms in the groups decreases.

Moving down the hierarchy from kingdom to species, means organisms are more closely related.

Taxonomists classify organisms according to how closely related they are. The more closely related, the more genes they will have in common. Two organisms in the same species will have almost all of their genes in common, allowing them to interbreed successfully. Classifying two species into the same genus means that they are sufficiently genetically different to prevent them from interbreeding, but they are still thought to be closely related and have descended from a recent common ancestor.

Binomial system

Many living organisms have common names, which may differ from one part of a country to another. This can be confusing, and even more confusing if a particular species needs to be named and described in a scientific research paper, which may be read by a scientist from a different country.

To overcome the problem, organisms are named according to the binomial system. This system was introduced by Linnaeus in 1753 and is based on using Latin as an international language. Each organism is given two names, the name of its genus and the name of its species. This system means that an organism is given precise identification worldwide, whereas the common name is not. The binomial system is still used successfully today because not only does each particular organism have its own unique scientific name but it also allows biologists to recognise that that two species are closely related, e.g. *Panthera leo* (lion) and *Panthera tigris* (tiger).

The five kingdom classification

Living organisms are divided into five large groups or kingdoms.

Prokaryotae
Unicellular organisms include bacteria and blue-green algae. They do not possess any internal cell membranes, nuclear membrane, endoplasmic reticulum, mitochondria or Golgi body. They have a cell wall but it is not made of cellulose.

Protoctista
These are mostly small eukaryotic organisms, with membrane-bound organelles and a nucleus with a nuclear membrane. In this kingdom are found the organisms that are neither plants nor animals nor fungi. The kingdom includes algae, the water moulds, the slime moulds and the protozoa.

Fungi
Eukaryotic, the body consisting of a network of threads called hyphae, forming a mycelium. There is a rigid cell wall made of chitin. They do not have photosynthetic pigments, and feeding is heterotrophic; all members of the group are either saprophytic or parasitic. In some sub-groups the hyphae have no cross-walls, but in others cross-walls, or septa, are present. Reproduction is by spores that lack flagella. Examples are *Penicillium*, yeast, mushroom.

Plants
Multicellular and carry out photosynthesis. The cells are eukaryotic, have cellulose walls, vacuoles containing cell sap, and chloroplasts containing photosynthetic pigments. The main plant phyla include mosses and liverworts, ferns, conifers and flowering plants.

Animals
Multicellular organisms, heterotrophic, eukaryotes, with cells lacking a cell wall, show nervous coordination.

quickfire

③ Why is it important for scientists to use Latin names for organisms mentioned in research papers?

Grade boost
You should learn the basic features which distinguish the five kingdoms.

quickfire

④ Some fungi are plant-like in appearance. Why are they placed in a separate kingdom to plants?

》 Pointer
The flowering plants (Angiosperms) are the most dominant plant group on Earth. They include all our major crops and are therefore an important food source. Their flowers have seeds that are enclosed in a fruit formed from the ovary wall.

≫ *Pointer*

95% of all animals are invertebrates and only 5% are vertebrates.

⑤ What is the binomial name for a human?

≫ *Pointer*

The description of fossils is mainly background information.

⑥ In which rock layers are the oldest fossils found?

The animal kingdom is divided into two main groups:

- Non-chordates, often called invertebrates. Examples include segmented worms, molluscs and arthropods.
- Chordates – all but the simplest of the chordates have a vertebral column or backbone and are therefore referred to as vertebrates and include fish, amphibians, reptiles, birds and mammals.

Classification of a human

The Latin name for our species is *Homo sapiens*.

The table gives the classification of a human.

Kingdom	Animalia (animals)
Phylum	Chordata (chordates)
Class	Mammalia (mammals)
Order	Primates (primates)
Family	Hominidae (hominids)
Genus	*Homo*
Species	*sapiens*

There are no other members of the genus *Homo* on Earth, but in the past there have been other species which scientists think should also be classified in this genus. They include *Homo habilis* and *Homo erectus*. The **fossil** record suggests that these two species were sufficiently different from *Homo sapiens* that the latter was not able to interbreed with them if they chanced to be on Earth at the same time.

Human evolution

Human evolution is a controversial subject and elaborate theories have been proposed in an attempt to explain how humans evolved. These various theories are based on the discovery and study of fossils.

Palaeontologists study fossil remains and place extinct animals and plants into geological sequence. By this means it is possible to suggest how one group may have evolved into another. The fact that fossils are formed in sedimentary rocks helps palaeontologists to do this. In the formation of sedimentary rocks, layers of silt harden, and layers form on top of each other. The resulting rock consists of a series of horizontal layers, or strata, with each layer containing fossils typical of the time when it was laid down. The oldest rocks, and therefore the earliest fossils, are contained in the lowest layers; the youngest rocks, and the most recent fossils, are in the later or uppermost layers. Rocks can often be dated precisely by radiometric dating techniques. Knowing the age of the rocks and a study of the fossil record tells scientists about the sequence and timing of the appearance of the major groups of living organisms.

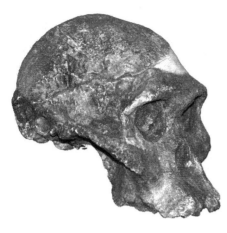

Early humanoid skull.

Key Term

Continental drift = the movement of the Earth's continents relative to each other by appearing to drift across the ocean bed.

The first humans

When studying human evolution the following points need to be considered:

- Human evolution should not be seen as a ladder with a series of steps leading directly from an ancestral anthropoid to *H.sapiens*. Instead, there have been many side-tracks leading to 'dead ends'. At times there have been several different species coexisting. Human evolution is more like a multi-branched tree than a ladder, with our species being the tip of the only twig that still lives.

- Our ancestors were not chimpanzees or any other modern ape. Chimpanzees, apes and humans represent divergent branches of the evolutionary tree that evolved from a common less-specialised ancestor.

- Various human characteristics did not evolve at the same time.

Different features, such as upright posture and an enlarged brain developed at different rates. In other words, our ancestors included those that walked upright but had a much less developed brain than ours.

Primates are subdivided into two groups – prosimians (premonkeys) and anthropoids which include monkeys, apes and humans.

The group includes humans as a biological species, together with many extinct species. Nearly all the primates are restricted to the tropics, with many living in tropical rain forests but with others in tropical savannah or scrub-land habitats. Only *Homo sapiens* is found over the entire surface of the Earth.

The study of human origins and evolution is called palaeoanthropology, and focuses on the last few million years of life on Earth when it is thought that humans and chimpanzees diverged from a common ancestor. Fossil evidence suggests that primates appeared around 60–65 million years ago (mya). Their common ancestor is believed to have been something like a present-day tree-shrew. This primitive primate diverged into apes and monkeys. Around 35–40 mya the geographical process of **continental drift** divided these animals into New World and Old World monkeys. It is from the Old World stock that apes, 'human-apes' and finally, hominids, developed.

Pointer

You are required to understand the stages that took place in the evolution of *Homo sapiens*. This involves characteristics such as an increase in brain size; development of manual dexterity and speech; development of an upright stance.

Much of the text is provided as background information.

quickfire

⑦ In geological time when did the common ancestor of humans and chimpanzees first appear on Earth?

Key Term

Phylogeny = the evolutionary relationship between organisms.

Grade boost

It is important to realise that evolutionary changes have taken place in the form of a **phylogenetic** tree rather than in a straight sequence as in a ladder.

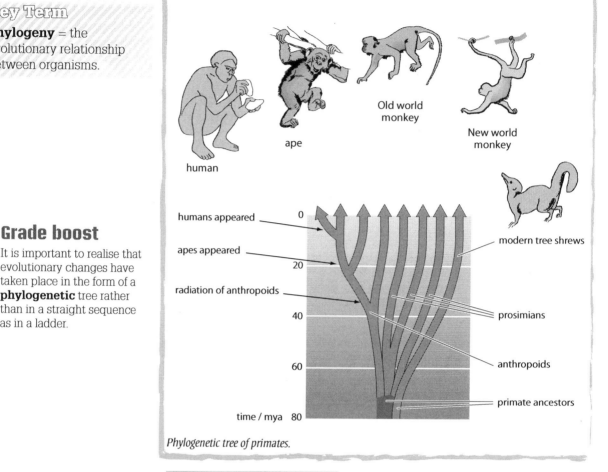

Phylogenetic tree of primates.

From apes to humans

There are several different ideas about how our species evolved. One possibility is that *Homo sapiens* evolved when a splinter group of an ancestral species became separated from the rest and gradually adapted to a different environment. Perhaps the ancestral species was adapted to living in dense tropical forest, while the splinter group became adapted to living in open grassland.

The earliest fossils that can be identified as apes have been found at many sites in Africa. They date from about 35 mya. At the time that apes and human-ape forms were evolving, the climate was changing dramatically. One reason was the drifting movements of the continents (the theory of continental drift). Around 16 mya Africa collided with Eurasia and allowed the migration from Africa of human-ape forms and early humans. Evidence for this has come from the discovery of fossils from many parts of the Earth, apart from Africa, and allowed scientists to record the later stages of human development as shown in the table on the next page.

Table showing steps from human-ape to *Homo sapiens*.

Name	When found (mya)	Features	Cranial volume (cm³)
Homo habilis	1.5–2.5	Made stone tools	750–800
Homo erectus	0.5–1.6	Used fire, lived in groups	850
Homo sapiens (included *H.sapiens neanderthalensis* until the last ice age)	Since 0.3	Hunter gatherers, buried their dead	1350

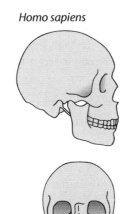

Homo habilis   Homo erectus   Homo sapiens

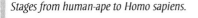

Stages from human-ape to Homo sapiens.

Some African, Asian, European and Australasian populations of *H.erectus* gave rise to diverse descendants that had even larger brains. Among these descendants were the Neanderthals (*Homo neanderthalensis*) who lived in Europe, the Middle East and parts of Asia from about 130,000 to 35,000 years ago. Neanderthal man was very human in appearance but generally stockier and more strongly built, compared with us. Neanderthals had slightly heavier brow ridges and less pronounced chins, but their brains, on average, were slightly larger than ours. Neanderthals used a wide range of tools, lived in caves or shelters made from tree branches and animal skins, and hunted wild animals such as mammoths and wild deer for food. Burial sites have been found suggesting that they followed religious practices and lived together in communities.

Key Term

Cranium = the part of the skeleton which encases the brain.

Pointer

Neanderthals are so named because their fossils were discovered in the Neander Valley in Germany.

quickfire

(8) How did Neanderthals differ physically from humans?

Pointer

Many misconceptions about human evolution were generated during the early part of the 20th century. Researchers put forward theories based on the discovery of a few teeth or a fragment of jawbone, which gave rise to new names for fossil forms that were undoubtedly the same fossil species as found by competing scientists.

Key Term

Gene pool = the total number of alleles in a particular population at a particular time.

Grade boost

This migration from Africa should not be considered as a mad dash for new territory. The gradual spread may have been associated with a change in diet to include a larger proportion of meat.

⑨ What features of the human body and behaviour have enabled humans to escape being restricted to living in the tropics?

⑩ What is meant by the term 'evolutionary dead end'?

quickfire

⑪ What is the essential difference between the two theories of the evolution of *Homo sapiens*?

How modern humans may have evolved

Two main theories have been proposed to explain how humans may have evolved:

1. The multiregional theory holds that *H.sapiens* evolved directly from *H.erectus* in different parts of the world.

2. The monogenesis or 'out of Africa' model, which suggests that only the African descendants of *Homo erectus* gave rise to modern humans. All other regional descendants, including Neanderthals, became extinct without contributing to the **gene pool** of modern man. Supporters of this theory believe that modern humans began spreading from Africa less than 100,000 years ago, giving rise to all the diverse populations of modern humans.

The debate about which theory is correct has been focused on the relationship between Neanderthals and the modern humans of Europe and the Middle East. The most famous European fossils of modern *H.sapiens* were found in caves in France. These fossils, dating back about 35,000 years, consisted of skulls and other bones that looked essentially like those of today's humans. But the oldest fully modern fossils of *H.sapiens*, about 100,000 years old, are found in Africa. Similar fossils of the same age have been discovered in caves in Israel. Near these caves were found other caves containing Neanderthal-like fossils. Evidence suggests that these two human types co-existed in this region for at least 40,000 years from the time modern forms appeared 100,000 years ago. It is argued that the persistence of these two forms during their time of co-existence means that these two human types did not interbreed. If this is correct then the Neanderthals of that region could not have been the ancestors of the modern humans that also lived there.

Recent DNA studies have been used to compare fossil DNA with that of a modern human. A sample of DNA was obtained from an unusually well-preserved Neanderthal fossil in Europe. Analysis indicated that the Neanderthal individual was genetically distinct from a modern European. This result supports the 'out of Africa' theory, but generalisations cannot be made from one specimen.

It is now generally believed that Neanderthals were evolutionary dead ends.

It is also generally accepted that the development and expansion of the more advanced *H.sapiens* occurred much later and that they did not interbreed with the other hominid groups that they encountered but replaced them through competition.

The evolutionary relationships of *H.habilis* and *H.erectus* are unclear, but since they overlap in time and space they do not form a single evolutionary sequence. More evidence is needed to clarify many issues involved with the evolution of humans.

Using genetic techniques to work out common ancestry

During the course of evolution when one species gives rise to another the new species will have some differences in the sequence of nucleotide bases in the DNA. Over time the new species will accumulate more differences in the DNA. Therefore one would expect species that are more closely related to show more similarity in their DNA base sequences than species that are more distantly related.

DNA analysis has been used to confirm evolutionary relationships and can reduce the mistakes made in classification due to **convergent evolution.**

- The technique of DNA hybridisation involves the extraction and comparison of the DNA of two species. The sequence of bases is compared and the more alike the sequences, the closer the organisms are related in terms of evolution.

- The sequence of amino acids in proteins is determined by DNA. Therefore the degree of similarity in the amino acid sequence of the same protein in two species will reflect how closely related the two species are. Part of the fibrinogen molecule of various mammals has been compared and the sequence has been found to differ in varying degrees from one species to another and this has enabled scientists to draw up a possible evolutionary tree for mammals.

- The proteins of different species can also be compared using immunological techniques. The principle behind this involves the fact that antibodies of one species will respond to specific antigens on proteins, such as albumin, in the blood serum of another. When antibodies respond to corresponding antigens a precipitate is formed. The greater the degree of precipitation the closer the evolutionary relationship.

To work out how closely related two species of primates are, such as humans and chimpanzees, the DNA strands from both species are extracted, separated and cut into fragments. The fragments from the two species are then mixed and analysed. This technique gives results which show that chimpanzees and humans have 97.6% DNA in common, whereas humans and rhesus monkeys have 91.1% of DNA in common. Recent studies using this technique have also shown that the hippopotamus and whale are closely related.

Immunological comparisons of human serum with that of other species.

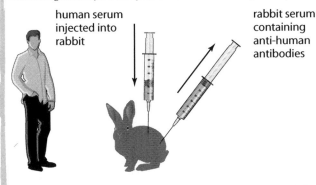

human serum
injected into
rabbit

rabbit serum
containing
anti-human
antibodies

rabbit serum
added to
other species

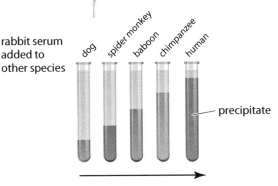

dog spider monkey baboon chimpanzee human

precipitate

increasing amount of precipitation
showing a closer evolutionary relationship

Key Term
Convergent evolution = the tendency of unrelated organisms to acquire similar structures.

quickfire

⑫ Using the technique of DNA hybridisation how is it possible to tell if two organisms are related in terms of evolution?

Grade boost
Comparing the DNA and proteins of different species helps scientists to determine the evolutionary relationships between them.

≫ Pointer
DNA comparisons suggest that the pathways to Neanderthals and modern humans diverged as much as 600,000 years ago.

Uptake of energy and nutrients

Processing food in the digestive system

Grade boost

Humans have a varied diet. The gut is divided into various parts along its length and each part is specialised to carry out particular steps in the processes of mechanical and chemical digestion as well as absorption

Grade boost

Consider revisiting the topic of 'enzymes' on page 26.

Heterotrophs cannot synthesise their major food requirements and so are dependent on a source of ready-made food. This food is needed as a source of energy for activities such as movement, and for the synthesis of body tissues. The organic molecules must be broken down by digestion and absorbed into the body tissues from the digestive system before utilisation in the body cells. Digestion and absorption take place in the gut, which is a long, hollow, muscular tube. The gut is organised to allow movement of its contents in one direction only.

Food is processed as it passes along the various regions of the gut. It is propelled along the gut by the process of **peristalsis.**

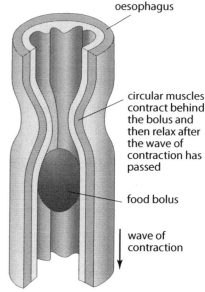

muscular wall of oesophagus

circular muscles contract behind the bolus and then relax after the wave of contraction has passed

food bolus

wave of contraction

The human gut performs four main functions:

Peristalsis

1. Ingestion is the taking in of food into the body through the mouth.

2. Digestion is the breakdown of large, insoluble food molecules into simple, soluble molecules by means of enzymes. Mechanical digestion in humans is achieved by the cutting and/or crushing action of the teeth, followed by the rhythmical contractions of the gut. The gut wall, particularly the stomach, has layers of muscle to fulfil this function. These are responsible for mixing the food and pushing it along the gut. The physical action also has an important role as it increases the surface area over which enzymes can act. The chemical action of digestion is achieved through the secretion of digestive enzymes.

3. Absorption is the passage of digested food through the gut wall into the blood.

4. Egestion is the elimination from the body of food that cannot be digested, e.g. cellulose cell walls of plants.

⑬ Define the term 'digestion'.

⑭ Define the term 'absorption'.

Functions of the gut.

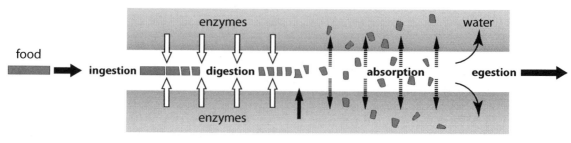

Structure of the human gut

Throughout its length from the mouth to the anus the gut wall consists of four tissue layers surrounding a cavity (lumen) of the gut.

- The outer serosa consists of a layer of tough connective tissue that protects the wall of the gut and reduces friction from other organs in the abdomen as the gut moves during the digestive process.
- The muscle layer consists of two layers of muscle running in different directions: the inner circular muscle and the outer longitudinal muscle.

  Collectively these muscles cause waves of muscular contractions, peristalsis, which propel food along the gut. Behind the bolus of food the circular muscles contract and the longitudinal muscles relax, thus helping move the food along.

- The sub-mucosa consists of connective tissue containing blood and lymph vessels to take away absorbed food products, as well as nerves that co-ordinate the muscular contractions involved in the process of peristalsis.
- The mucosa is the innermost layer and lines the wall of the gut. It secretes mucus which lubricates and protects the mucosa. In some regions of the gut this layer secretes digestive juices, in others it absorbs digested food.

General structure of the gut wall.

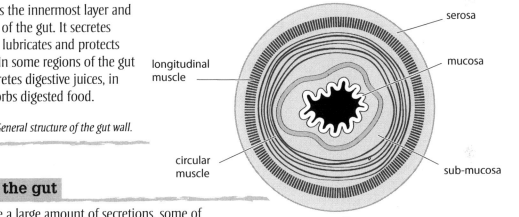

serosa

mucosa

longitudinal muscle

circular muscle

sub-mucosa

Glands in the gut

Glands produce a large amount of secretions, some of which contain digestive enzymes.

The glands of the gut are of three types:

1. Large glands found outside the gut with secretions passing through tubes or ducts into the gut cavity:
   - Salivary glands which secrete saliva into the mouth.
   - Liver which secretes bile into the duodenum.
   - Pancreas which secretes pancreatic juice into the duodenum.
2. Glands in the form of cells in the sub-mucosa:
   - Glands which secrete mucus into the duodenum.
3. Glands in the form of cells in the mucosa:
   - Gastric glands in the stomach wall which secrete gastric juice into the stomach.
   - Glands found at the base of the villus in the small intestine, which secrete enzymes into the small intestine.

> ## Grade boost
> Be prepared to label a given diagram of the wall of the gut.

> ## » Pointer
> Be prepared to provide functions of various parts for various tissues of the gut wall. The outer layer serves to protect, the muscle layer propels food along the gut, the sub-mucosa contains blood vessels to supply nutrients and nerves to co-ordinate activities, the inner layer produces secretions.

 **quickfire**

⑮ Name the four layers of the gut wall.

> ## Grade boost
> Glands are of two main types: collections of cells which pass their secretions to the site of action through ducts; individual cells which pass secretions directly to the site of action.

Key Term

Mucus = a slimy glycoprotein, secreted by gland cells in the mucosa, forming a protective layer. It also lubricates food as it passes through the gut.

Grade boost

Before food is digested it must be broken down mechanically. This takes place by means of the teeth, stomach, and by the peristaltic action of the muscular layers of the gut wall.

quickfire

⑯ Name the digested products of each of the following: carbohydrates, fats, proteins.

Digestion

The absorption of nutrients by the gut epithelial cells is only possible if the large molecules, carbohydrates, fats and proteins are first broken down or digested into smaller products by means of enzymes. Different enzymes are required to carry out digestion of the different food substrates and usually more than one type of enzyme is needed for the complete digestion of a particular food.

- Carbohydrates (polysaccharides) are first broken down into disaccharides and then into monosaccharides. The enzyme amylase hydrolyses starch to the disaccharide maltose but another enzyme, maltase, is required to break down the maltose to the monosaccharide glucose.

- Proteins are broken down into polypeptides, then dipeptides, and finally into amino acids. The general name given to the protein-digesting enzymes is peptidases. Proteins are extremely large molecules so endopeptidases hydrolyse peptide bonds within the protein molecule and exopeptidases hydrolyse peptide bonds at the ends of these shorter polypeptides.

- Fats are broken down to fatty acids and glycerol by just one enzyme, lipase.

Regional specialisations of the human gut

The mouth

Mechanical digestion begins in the mouth when food is chewed using the teeth. The food is also mixed with saliva from the salivary glands. Saliva is a watery secretion containing **mucus** and salivary amylase together with some mineral ions which help to keep the pH in the mouth slightly alkaline, the optimum pH for amylase. Saliva is important for lubricating food before it is swallowed. Amylase breaks down starch to maltose. After chewing, the bolus of food is swallowed and mucus lubricates its passage down the oesophagus.

The stomach

Food enters the stomach and is kept there by the contraction of two rings of muscles, one at the stomach entrance and one at the junction with the duodenum. Food may stay in the stomach for up to four hours and during this time the muscles of the stomach wall contract rhythmically and mix up the food with gastric juice secreted by glands in the stomach wall. Gastric juice contains acid that gives the stomach contents a pH of 2.0. As well as providing the optimum pH for the enzymes,

Structure of the digestive system.

mouth —
oesophagus
liver
bile duct
gall bladder
small intestine { duodenum / ileum
stomach
colon
caecum
appendix
rectum
anus

the acid kills most bacteria in the food. Gastric juice also contains peptidase enzymes which hydrolyse the protein to polypeptides. Mucus is important in forming a lining to protect the stomach wall from the enzymes and acid as well as assisting in the movement of food within the stomach.

The gastric glands in the stomach wall are simple tubular structures containing peptic cells, oxyntic cells and goblet cells.

Stomach wall.

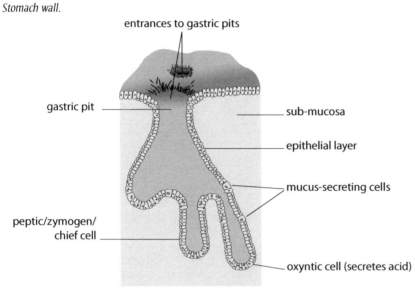

- Peptic cells (chief cells) secrete the protein-digesting enzyme, pepsin, as an inactive precursor, pepsinogen. This prevents the enzyme from damaging the stomach tissues. Pepsinogen remains inactive until it reaches the lumen of the stomach where it is activated by hydrochloric acid and the resulting pepsin begins the breakdown of proteins to polypeptides. Pepsin is prevented from damaging the stomach wall by the secretion of mucus.

- Oxyntic cells secrete hydrochloric acid which makes the stomach contents acid; the acid conditions kill off many pathogenic bacteria as well as activating the protein-digesting enzymes.

- Goblet cells secrete mucus. This forms a protective layer on the stomach wall, thus preventing pepsin and hydrochloric acid from breaking down the gastric mucosa. Mucus also helps the movement of food within the stomach.

Rennin is also secreted in an inactive form by peptic cells. It is activated by acid and coagulates the soluble protein in milk. This is important in babies as it allows the semi-solid product to remain in the stomach for a longer period of time enabling digestion to take place more effectively.

The small intestine

The small intestine is divided into two regions, the duodenum and the ileum.

Relaxation of the muscle at the base of the stomach allows the partially digested food into the duodenum a little at a time. The duodenum makes up about the first 20cm of the small intestine and receives secretions from both the liver and the pancreas.

>> **Pointer**

Different enzymes have different pH optima and therefore function in particular areas of the gut.

Grade boost

Throughout this section highlight the digestion of carbohydrate, fats and proteins in three different colours.
This will help you follow the digestion of the separate chemicals through the various parts of the gut.

quickfire

(17) Why are certain enzymes secreted in an inactive form?

>> **Pointer**

You should be able to explain how the different regions of the gut achieve different pH values, e.g. such as the walls of the duodenum secrete an alkaline juice; oxyntic cells secrete hydrochloric acid.

>> **Pointer**

In an exam you would not be expected to write a complete essay on the topic of digestion. Exam essays usually ask for the digestion of either proteins or carbohydrates.

Emulsification = the breakdown of large fat globules into smaller, uniformly distributed particles.

quickfire

⑱ State the function of:
1. Bile
2. Mucus.

quickfire

⑲ Name the three enzymes contained in pancreatic juice.

Endo- and exopeptidase.

endopeptidases hydrolyse peptide bonds within the protein chain, leaving smaller polypeptide sections

exopeptidases hydrolyse peptide bonds on terminal amino acids

quickfire

⑳ How do endo- and exopeptidases differ in the way they function?

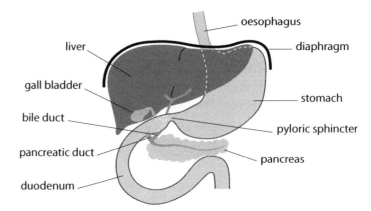

Duodenum, gall bladder and liver.

- Bile is produced in the liver and stored in the gall bladder from where it passes into the duodenum via the bile duct. It contains no enzymes but the bile salts are important in emulsifying the lipids present in the food. **Emulsification** is achieved by lowering the surface tension of the lipids causing large globules to break up into tiny droplets. This enables the action of the enzyme lipase to be more efficient as the lipid droplets now have a much larger surface area. Bile also helps to neutralise the acidity of the food as it comes from the stomach.

- Pancreatic juice is secreted from the exocrine glands in the pancreas and enters the duodenum through the pancreatic duct. It contains a number of different enzymes:
  - Endopeptidases which hydrolyse protein to polypeptides.
  - Amylase which breaks down any remaining starch to maltose.
  - Lipase which hydrolyses lipids into fatty acids and glycerol.

The walls of the duodenum contain glands, called Brunner's glands, which secrete an alkaline juice and mucus. The alkaline juice helps to keep the contents of the small intestine at the correct pH for enzyme action, and the mucus is for lubrication and protection.

Enzymes secreted by groups of cells at the bottom of crypts of Lieberkühn, complete digestion. See diagram on the next page.

- Maltase hydrolyses maltose into two glucose molecules.
- Sucrase hydrolyses sucrose to glucose and fructose.
- Endopeptidases and exopeptidases complete the digestion of polypeptides to amino acids.
- Dipeptidase breaks down dipeptides to amino acids.

The end products of carbohydrate digestion are all monosaccharides. The final stage of carbohydrate digestion is intracellular, as disaccharides are absorbed by the plasma membrane of the epithelial cells before being broken down into monosaccharides.

Absorption

Up to this point the breakdown of carbohydrates, proteins and fats has been considered. The following describes how the soluble products of digestion are absorbed into the body.

The region called the ileum is well adapted for absorption. In humans it is very long and the lining is folded to give a large surface area compared with a smooth tube. On the folds are numerous finger-like projections called villi. On the surface of the villi are epithelial cells with microscopic projections called **microvilli**. These increase the surface area of the cell membrane of the epithelial cells for absorption.

Absorption takes place mainly in the small intestine. Because energy is required for active absorption, the epithelial cells also contain large numbers of mitochondria.

- Glucose and amino acids are absorbed across the epithelium of the villi by a combination of diffusion and active transport. They pass into the capillary network that supplies each villus. As carbohydrates are being digested continuously there is normally a greater concentration of glucose within the small intestine than in the blood. Glucose therefore diffuses into the blood down a concentration gradient. As glucose is needed for respiration it is continuously being transported in the blood to the cells. As diffusion is a slow process not all the available glucose can be absorbed in this way and some would pass out of the body. However, this does not occur as glucose is also being transported by active transport.

Key Term

Microvilli = small finger-like projections from the cell membrane that increase the surface area.

quickfire

㉑ Into which parts of the villus are the end products of digestion absorbed?

Grade boost

The transport of digested products involves the process of diffusion or active transport. Check which method is involved with specific products.

Epithelial cells of the small intestine and the absorption process .

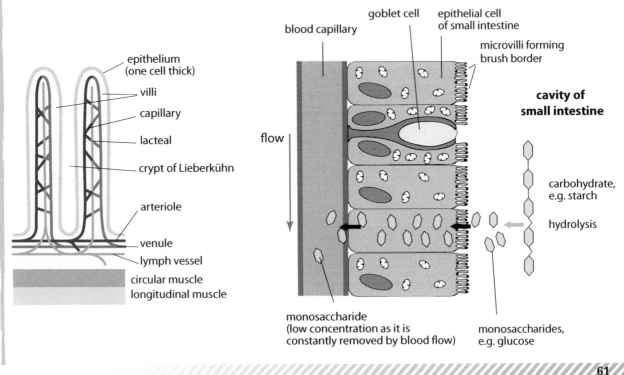

Small intestine

epithelium (one cell thick)
villi
capillary
lacteal
crypt of Lieberkühn
arteriole
venule
lymph vessel
circular muscle
longitudinal muscle

blood capillary
goblet cell
epithelial cell of small intestine
microvilli forming brush border

cavity of small intestine

flow

carbohydrate, e.g. starch

hydrolysis

monosaccharide (low concentration as it is constantly removed by blood flow)

monosaccharides, e.g. glucose

- Fatty acids and glycerol are passed into the lacteal. This is a blindly ending **lymph** capillary found in the centre of each villus. Fatty acids and glycerol are transported in the lymphatic system which ultimately opens into the blood stream at the thoracic duct.

To summarise, the following methods of transport occur:

- Fatty acids, glycerol, glucose and most vitamins pass through the membrane of the epithelial cells by diffusion.

- However, disaccharides, amino acids and dipeptides require energy in the form of ATP for absorption by active uptake.

- Dipeptides and disaccharides are then digested intracellularly into simple amino acids.

- Glucose and amino acids then diffuse from the epithelial cells into the blood.

The large intestine

The large intestine is about 1.5 metres long and is divided into the caecum, the colon and the rectum. Water and mineral salts are absorbed from the colon along with vitamins secreted by micro-organisms living in the colon. These bacteria are responsible for making vitamin K and folic acid. By the time it reaches the rectum, indigestible food is in a semi-solid condition. It consists of residues of undigested cellulose, bacteria and sloughed cells and passes along the colon to be egested as faeces. This process is called defecation.

Fate of digested products after absorption

With the completion of the processes of digestion and absorption the soluble food products are carried in the bloodstream to the tissues for assimilation or to provide energy.

- Glucose is absorbed from the blood by cells, for energy release in respiration.

- Amino acids are absorbed for protein synthesis, any excess cannot be stored so is **deaminated** whereby the removed amino groups are converted to urea and the remainder to carbohydrate and stored.

- Lipids are used for membranes and hormones; any excess is stored as fat.

Conditions affecting the digestive system

To sustain a healthy lifestyle a person needs to exercise and have sufficient sleep as well as having a balanced and varied diet. There is a tendency to think of diseases as being caused by the invasion of the body by other organisms. However, there are a number of other causes of disease including inherited disease, and deficiency diseases caused by an inadequate diet.

Grade boost

When studying diseases, learn the causes, symptoms and treatment of each disease.

Cancer

Cancer can occur in various areas of the digestive system, for example cancer of the stomach, liver, pancreas, bowel, etc. Cancer describes a disease characterised by the progressive and uncontrolled growth of abnormal cells.

The symptoms produced by different kinds of cancers depend on the site of growth, the tissue of origin, and the extent of the growth. Symptoms may be a direct feature of the growth, bleeding or disruption of the function of the organ affected. There may be a rapid weight loss without an apparent cause. With bowel cancer there may be a change in bowel habits and blood in the faeces.

There are a number of different methods for treating cancer:

- Chemotherapy involves the action of drugs that act selectively on the cancer cells. Anti-cancer drugs act either by destroying tumour cells or stopping them from multiplying. Unfortunately, the drugs used may also affect normal tissue because the drugs act on all rapidly dividing cells, not just tumour cells. They may cause destruction of white blood cells, hair loss, sterility, and affect the mouth and intestines.

- Radiotherapy involves using ionising radiation, normally a source of damage to DNA, to treat cancer tumours. As the radiation passes through the diseased tissue it destroys or slows down the development of abnormal cells. Provided the correct dosage of radiation is given, normal cells suffer very little and there is no long-term damage. Side effects are usually short-lived and involve minor burning of the skin and some localised hair loss.

- Surgical removal may be necessary to remove primary tumours and is often combined with radiotherapy and/or chemotherapy. In the case of bowel cancer, surgery is the main method of treatment.

Research suggests that there is a link between bowel cancer and diet. Experts think that about a quarter of all cancer deaths are caused by an unhealthy diet or obesity. Our diet influences the risk of many cancers, including cancers of the mouth, oesophagus, stomach and bowel. The risk of cancer can be reduced by eating a healthy, balanced diet that is high in fibre, fruit and vegetables, and low in red and processed meat and saturated fat. Some evidence also suggests that certain diet supplements such as calcium and possibly folic acid may reduce risk.

quickfire

㉓ What is the main symptom of bowel cancer?

Grade boost

Early diagnosis of cancer is essential. A simple bowel screening test can be carried out at home. The test determines if there is hidden blood in the faeces.

quickfire

㉔ Explain why patients with colon cancer and those who have had their colon surgically removed, are likely to suffer from symptoms of dehydration.

㉕ Explain why people with coeliac disease sometimes suffer from deficiency diseases.

Grade boost

Gluten is found in wheat, barley and rye. It leads to loss of villus height and a breakdown of microvilli.

㉖ State which food type is essential in the diet to reduce the development of diverticular disease.

㉗ State one major cause of a peptic ulcer.

㉘ State one factor which aggravates a stomach ulcer.

quickfire

㉙ State one form of treatment for a stomach ulcer.

≫ Pointer

Factors aggravating an ulcer include: eating spicy food; drinking caffeine and alcohol; smoking; stress may also worsen the symptoms.

Coeliac disease

It is thought that as many as 1% of the population may have coeliac disease. It is caused by a protein, gluten, found in wheat, rye and barley. Upon exposure to gluten an enzyme in the body modifies the protein and the immune system reacts with the bowel tissue causing an inflammatory reaction. This leads to a flattening of the villi of the small intestine and this interferes with the absorption of digestive products.

Symptoms can range from tiredness and lethargy to severe symptoms where the sufferer loses weight and becomes acutely ill. The only effective treatment is a life-long gluten-free diet.

Diverticular disease

Many people have small pouches in the colon of the large intestine. These pouches, called diverticula, bulge outwards through weak spots. The condition of having diverticula is called diverticulosis. It is a condition that becomes more common with age. When the pouches become infected or inflamed the condition is called diverticulitis, which happens to 10–25% of people with diverticulosis.

Symptoms of diverticulosis include mild cramp, bloating, and constipation. However, diverticulitis is more serious with abdominal pain. If infection is the cause, nausea, vomiting, chills, cramping and constipation may also occur. Diverticulitis can lead to bleeding, perforation, tearing or blockage and can become serious if untreated.

It is thought that the cause of diverticular disease is a low fibre diet, for example eating an excess of processed foods containing refined, low fibre flour. The treatment of diverticulosis involves eating a high fibre diet and prescribing mild pain medications to help relieve symptoms. Diverticulitis responds well to a course of antibiotics.

Peptic ulcer

A peptic ulcer is an erosion of the lining of the wall of the stomach. This may be due to an increase in the production of acid or when the mucus lining is damaged. Two major causes of peptic ulcers are infection with bacteria called *Helicobacter pylori*, or the long-term use of medicines such as anti-inflammatory drugs or aspirin. The most common symptoms of gastric ulcers are constant stomach pain made worse by eating, weight loss, nausea and vomiting.

H.pylori is thought to weaken the protective mucus lining of the stomach allowing stomach acid to get through and cause damage. Both the acid and bacteria irritate the stomach lining causing an ulcer. Seven out of ten people with a gastric ulcer are infected with *H.pylori*.

The treatment involves a combination of medicines:

- Antibiotics to clear the body of *H.pylori*.
- Drugs to reduce stomach acid.
- Drugs to protect the lining of the stomach.

Gas exchange

All living organisms exchange gases with the environment. They need oxygen to convert organic molecules, such as glucose, into energy by the process of respiration. In turn, waste gases have to be removed. The body needs energy in order to carry out all the processes of the body. The two most important factors determining the energy requirements of an individual are **metabolic rate** and physical activity. Apart from the energy needed to keep the body 'ticking over' at rest (called basal metabolic rate) the more active an individual is the more energy is needed. The human is an advanced, relatively large, active animal and so has a high metabolic rate. Humans therefore need a lot of energy and thus have a high requirement for oxygen. In order to make gas exchange more efficient, humans, in common with most other land animals, have developed a specialised exchange surface, the lungs, to compensate for the high oxygen demand. These animals need a ventilation mechanism to supply the respiratory surfaces with a fresh supply of oxygen and to maintain diffusion gradients.

In order to achieve the maximum rate of diffusion a respiratory surface must:

- Have a sufficiently large surface area relative to the volume of the organism to satisfy the needs of the organism.
- Be thin – so that diffusion paths are short.
- Be permeable – to allow the respiratory gases through.
- Be moist – to allow a medium in which gases can dissolve.

Problems associated with increase in size

In simple single-celled organisms such as *Amoeba* the gas exchange surface is the cell membrane. The organism lives in water and the diffusion of gases occurs over the whole of the body surface. A single cell has a large surface area compared with its volume. It is said to have a large surface area to volume ratio. The membrane is thin, moist, and the diffusion paths are short. The efficiency of gaseous diffusion satisfies the needs of the organism.

However, a limit to how large a cell can become is reached when the diffusion path is so long that the process of diffusion becomes inefficient. In terms of evolution, the only way that organisms could become larger was to aggregate cells together, that is, to become multicellular. However, the larger the organism, the smaller is the surface area to volume ratio. Also, materials need to be exchanged between different organs as well as between the organs and the environment. Diffusion throught the surface is insufficient to meet the gaseous requirements of the organism. In effect, the rate of the process of diffusion is too slow.

Key Term

Metabolic rate = the rate at which energy is used up in the body.

≫ Pointer

Gas exchange is the process by which oxygen reaches cells and carbon dioxide is removed from them. It should not be confused with respiration.

30 Name three factors that affect the rate of diffusion of substances into cells.

≫ Pointer

If you find the concept of surface area to volume ratio difficult, consider it this way. If the overall shape is kept the same, an increase in size means an increase in surface area but also increased distance from the surface to the centre of the organism.

31 Why do large multicellular animals like a human require specialised exchange surfaces?

The human respiratory system

>> **Pointer**

The main cause of air being forced out during normal breathing (at rest) is the recoil of the elastic lungs.

Grade boost

Be prepared to label a given diagram of the respiratory system.

quickfire

㉜ List in the correct order the structures that air passes through from the gas exchange surface to the atmosphere.

quickfire

㉝ What is the function of cartilage in the trachea?

Grade boost

The diffusion pathway is short as the walls of the alveoli are one cell thick and the blood capillaries have a single layer of endothelial cells.

>> **Pointer**

The percentage of oxygen in the alveolus is less than in inspired air because the latter mixes with air already in the lungs. This has a lower percentage of oxygen.

The lungs consist of a branching network of tubes called bronchioles arising from a pair of bronchi. The lungs are enclosed within an airtight compartment, the thorax, at the base of which is a dome-shaped sheet of muscle called the diaphragm. The lungs are supported and protected by the rib cage. The ribs can be moved by the intercostals, the muscles between them. This enables the lungs to be ventilated so that air is constantly being replenished. Air is drawn into the lungs via a flexible airway called the trachea.

Human respiratory system.

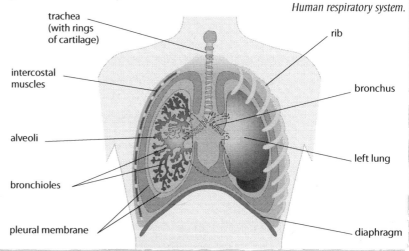

Gas exchange in the alveolus

The gas exchange surfaces or alveoli provide a very large surface area relative to the volume of the body. They are well suited as a gas exchange surface because the walls are thin, providing a short diffusion path. Each alveolus is covered by an extensive capillary network to maintain diffusion gradients, because blood is always taking oxygen away from the alveolus and returning with carbon dioxide. Deoxygenated blood enters the capillaries surrounding the alveolus. Oxygen diffuses out of the alveolus into the blood in the capillary. Carbon dioxide diffuses out of the capillary into the air in the alveolus.

Table showing the % composition of air in the lungs.

	Inspired air	Alveolar air	Expired air
Oxygen	20.95	13.80	16.40
Carbon dioxide	0.04	5.50	4.00
Nitrogen	79.01	80.70	79.60
Water	variable	saturated	saturated

Air flows down towards the lungs through the trachea and bronchi. These are lined by cells, called epithelial cells, which remove particles from the air before it reaches the lungs. There are two main types of cells making up the epithelial lining – ciliated cells and goblet cells. Cilia are tiny extensions of the cytoplasm that are found on the free surface of the cells. The function of the goblet cells is to secrete mucus.

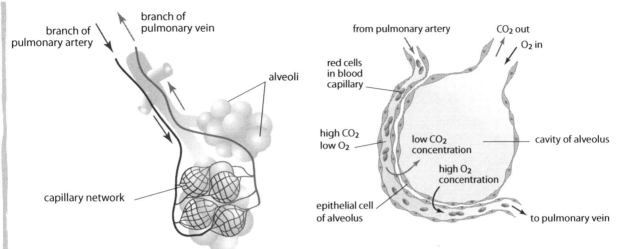

Alveoli   *Gas exchange in alveolus.*

When particles in the air, such as dust, bacteria and pollen, are breathed in they are trapped in the mucus. The cilia sweep the mucus upwards to the back of the throat. The mucus is then swallowed. This makes sure that the particles do not reach the lungs.

Ventilation of the lungs

Mammals ventilate their lungs by negative pressure breathing, forcing air down into the lungs. That is, if air is to enter the lungs then the pressure inside them must be lower than atmospheric pressure.

Inspiration or breathing in is an active process since muscle contraction requires energy.

- The external intercostal muscles contract.
- The ribs are pulled upwards and outwards.
- At the same time, the diaphragm muscles contract, causing it to flatten.
- Both actions increase the volume of the thorax.
- This results in a reduction of pressure in the lungs.
- As the atmospheric air pressure is now greater than the pressure in the lungs, air is forced into the lungs.

Grade boost

The essential features of exchange surfaces are lungs which supply a large surface area, increased by alveoli, lined with moisture for the dissolving of gases, thin walls to shorten the diffusion path and an extensive capillary network for rapid diffusion and transport, to maintain diffusion gradients.

≫ Pointer

Expiration or breathing out is a mainly passive process and is essentially the opposite of inspiration.

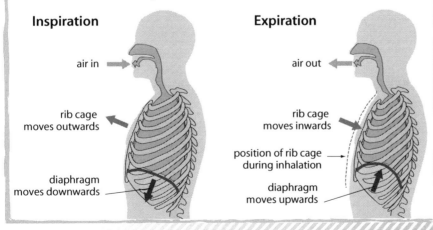

Movement of the ribs and diaphragm during ventilation.

Surfactant

Lining the thorax and surrounding each lung are pleural membranes, between which is a cavity containing pleural fluid. When breathing, this fluid acts as a lubricant, allowing friction-free movement against the inner wall of the thorax. To prevent the alveoli from collapsing when breathing out, an anti-sticking chemical, called a surfactant, covers their surfaces and reduces the surface tension.

One of the most common and immediate problems facing premature babies is difficulty in breathing. The most common cause is respiratory distress syndrome (RDS). In RDS the infant's immature lungs do not produce sufficient surfactant. Immediately after birth and several times afterwards an artificial surfactant can be administered. Although, for a while, most premature babies will need to be placed in a ventilator, the use of artificial surfactant greatly decreases the amount of time that infants spend on the ventilator.

>> **Pointer**
A natural surfactant is present in the lungs. The surfactant lowers the surface tension keeping the alveoli open.

Investigating human breathing by measuring lung capacity

The **spirometer** consists of an air-filled chamber of about 6 dm³ capacity suspended over water. The lid or float of the chamber is arranged so that it rises and falls as the subject breathes in and out through the mouthpiece. A pen connected to the float moves over a rotating chart, recording movements against time. The movements of the chamber are recorded on a kymograph trace as shown on the next page. The spirometer chamber may be filled with atmospheric air that is breathed in (inspired). Soda lime is used to absorb all the carbon dioxide from the expired air before it goes back into the chamber.

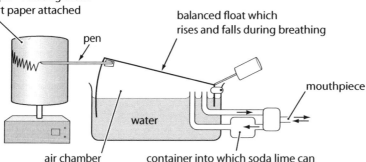

kymograph – rotating drum with chart paper attached

pen

balanced float which rises and falls during breathing

mouthpiece

water

air chamber

container into which soda lime can be placed to absorb carbon dioxide

Spirometer.

>> **Pointer**
You should understand the principles of spirometry and be able to interpret spirometer data in the form of a spirometer trace recorded on a kymograph. However, you are **not** required to carry out practical work using a spirometer.

Human lungs have a volume of about 5 dm³, but at rest only about 0.45 dm³ of this will be exchanged. This is called **tidal volume**. With increasing activity both the frequency and depth of inspiration will increase. **Vital capacity** is the total volume of air that can be expired after a maximum inspiration. Even after maximum expiration, about 1.5 dm³ of air remains in the lungs. This is called the **residual volume**.

The rate at which a person breathes is expressed as the ventilation rate.

Ventilation rate = tidal volume × number of breaths per minute

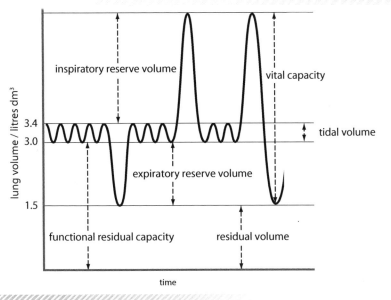

Human lung capacity.

Respiratory disease

Lung diseases are a major cause of illness and death in society. Two disorders that affect lung function are asthma and emphysema.

Asthma

This condition is a reaction, usually allergic, characterised by attacks of wheezing and difficulty in breathing. It is a common ailment in children and affects about one in twenty of the overall population. Attacks are brought on by spasms of the smooth muscles that lie in the walls of the bronchioles causing the passageways to close partially. The obstruction of these air passages means that more effort is needed to deliver sufficient air to the lungs. Usually the mucus membranes that line the respiratory passageways become irritated and secrete excessive amounts of mucus that may clog the bronchi and bronchioles and worsen the attack.

The possible causes of asthma include air pollution and allergens. The most common allergens are house dust mites, animal fur and feathers, and pollen. Drugs taken in aerosol form are prescribed as an inhalant. They give rapid relief by causing the smooth muscle lining the bronchioles to relax, so widening the airways. Steroids reduce the amount of inflammation of the bronchioles.

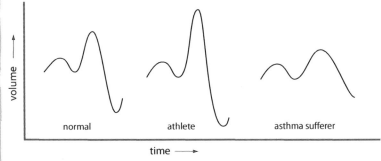

Spirometer traces of a healthy person, a healthy athlete, and an asthma sufferer.

Grade boost

A common error is to describe a constriction of the trachea rather than the bronchioles.

>> *Pointer*

By the end of their teenage years more than half the children with asthma will be relieved of the condition.

Grade boost

Be prepared to describe the causes, symptoms and treatment of respiratory diseases.

 quickfire

㉞ What feature distinguishes the asthma sufferer's trace from the healthy trace?

Explain the cause of this feature of the asthma sufferer's trace.

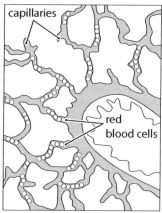

Healthy lung

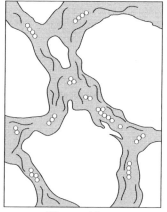

Diseased lung

*TS through a healthy lung and a lung.
from an emphysema sufferer.*

quickfire

㉟ Using the diagram above state how the surface area of the lung is affected? What effect does this have on the ability to take up oxygen?

⚑ Grade boost

Plan for an exam essay on smoking as follows: List the diseases caused by smoking; list the chemicals in cigarette smoke; describe the effect of each chemical on the lungs.

Emphysema

This is a condition which develops over a period of about 20 years and is impossible to diagnose until the lungs have been irreversibly damaged. It should not be confused with asthma, although it shares common symptoms such as breathlessness and a shortage of oxygen. In the early stages of emphysema the only symptom is breathlessness but as this gets progressively worse, the sufferer becomes so disabled that they cannot even get out of bed.

In emphysema the walls of the alveoli lose their elasticity and remain filled with air during expiration. As the condition progresses the walls of the alveoli break down and many alveoli may merge to form larger air sacs with a reduced overall volume. The lungs become permanently inflated because they have lost their elasticity. Little, if any, exchange of gases can take place across the stretched and damaged air sacs.

Emphysema is generally caused by long-term irritation. Air pollution, occupational exposure to industrial dust and cigarette smoke are the most common irritants. Cigarette smoke not only deactivates a protein crucial in preventing emphysema but also prevents the repair of affected lung tissue. Emphysema cannot be cured and the disease cannot be reversed. The only way to minimise the chance of developing emphysema is to not smoke at all or to give up smoking. If you smoke, the chances are that some damage has already taken place. However, giving up smoking can significantly reduce the rate of further deterioration.

Effects of smoking

Chronic obstructive pulmonary disease (COPD) is a condition in which the airflow into and out of the lungs gradually and progressively becomes more and more obstructed. COPD happens in everyone to a certain extent as they get older but is greatly accelerated and worsened by smoking. It is thought that 300 million people die from COPD each year and that between 80% and 90% of these cases are caused by smoking cigarettes!

Cigarette smoke contains a wide range of different chemicals; the three most hazardous of these are tar, nicotine and carbon monoxide. These chemicals cause tissue damage resulting in emphysema. In place of millions of minute alveoli the lung becomes a mass of larger spaces, widely separated from blood capillaries. The total surface area for gaseous exchange is greatly reduced.

The tar in tobacco smoke produces two reactions in the lungs. The goblet cells in the epithelium of the air passages are stimulated to over-produce mucus. The ciliated cells, which waft the mucus out of the air passages, do not work and may be destroyed. This results in a build-up of mucus in the bronchial passages and bacteria and viruses multiply in the mucus. The result is chronic bronchitis.

While COPD causes about 15% of smoking-related deaths, lung cancer causes almost double that number. Smokers are almost 20 times more likely to die from lung cancer than non-smokers. Tar collects in the lungs as the tobacco smoke cools. Tar contains a mixture of many toxic chemicals. Some of these chemicals cause cancer and are known as **carcinogens.** These substances affect the control of cell division resulting in a mass of disorganised tissue, known as a tumour. As the tumour grows it displaces other tissues. Eventually this can lead to a blockage of the airways or other parts of the lungs. Cancerous cells may break away from the original tumour and begin to form tumours in other parts of the body. If this happens the chances of survival are low.

Nicotine is the substance that makes tobacco addictive. When a person is trying to give up smoking they experience withdrawal symptoms due to the absence of nicotine in the body. Nicotine stimulates the release of the hormone adrenaline into the blood stream. Adrenaline has a number of important effects on the body. For example, it produces the 'flight or fight' response, which prepares the body for physical activity by increasing heart rate and raising blood pressure. Many long-term smokers develop raised blood pressure and this can lead to other problems including atherosclerosis, coronary heart disease and strokes. Atherosclerosis is the build-up of fatty deposits on the inner walls of arteries making them thicker and inflexible. This in turn leads to a narrowing of the vessels, which reduces the flow of blood. The heart therefore has to exert more pressure to get the blood through.

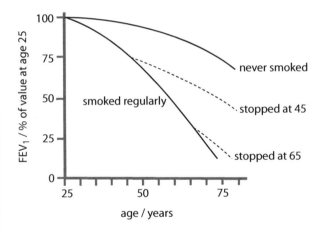

Graph showing how forced expiration volume (FEV$_1$) changes with age in smokers and . non-smokers.

Carbon monoxide is a gas found in tobacco smoke. Haemoglobin combines more readily with carbon monoxide than it does with oxygen! In smokers this causes reduction in the amount of oxygen in the blood and so the heart has to work harder to supply the body with the oxygen it needs. In the short term this means that the smoker is unable to take part effectively in physical activity. In the long term, high levels of carbon monoxide can lead to hardening of the arteries, especially the coronary arteries supplying the heart muscle.

Key Term

Carcinogen = chemical which causes cancer.

>> Pointer

Atherosclerosis, heart disease and stroke are studied in more detail on pages 80–83

>> Pointer

FEV$_1$ is measured using a peak flow meter. The patient blows as hard as possible into a mouthpiece and the distance a marker moves in a tube is measured.

quickfire

(36) Describe the changes in FEV$_1$ which occur as a non-smoker gets older. Compare this with the FEV$_1$ of a life-long smoker.

Grade boost

Be prepared to answer exam questions involving the interpretation of graphs.

>> Pointer

In recent years the effects of passive smoking have been recognised. A smoker may breathe in only 15% of the smoke produced from a cigarette, while the remaining 85% is released into the air. In a confined space non-smokers can breathe in the smoke and consequently suffer from the effects. As a result, legislation banning smoking in public places came into effect in England and Wales in 2007.

Key Term

Macrophage = white blood cells called monocytes travel in the blood. Once they settle in organs they develop into macrophages. These initiate the immune response displaying antigens for recognition by lymphocytes (see page 93).

>> **Pointer**

The function of red blood cells in relation to the transport of respiratory gases is studied in detail on pages 85–87.

quickfire

③⑦ What features of red blood cells make them well suited for the carriage of oxygen?

quickfire

③⑧ State two differences between the structure of red and white blood cells.

>> **Pointer**

White blood cells are concerned with the body's protection against infection. This is dealt with on pages 90–94.

Transport to and from exchange surfaces

Humans require a transport system to take materials from cells to exchange surfaces and from exchange surfaces to cells. Materials also have to be transported between the exchange surface and the environment, as well as to different organs in the body.

The transport system in humans has the following common features:

- A suitable medium, blood, in which to carry materials.
- A closed system of vessels that contains the blood and forms a branching network to distribute it to all parts of the body.
- The heart, which acts as a pump for moving the blood within vessels.
- Valves to maintain the flow in one direction.
- A respiratory pigment, haemoglobin, which increases the volume of oxygen that can be transported.

Structure and functions of blood

Blood is a tissue made up of cells (45%) in fluid plasma (55%).

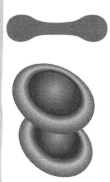

Red blood cells

Red blood cells or erythrocytes contain the pigment haemoglobin, the main function of which is to transport oxygen from the lungs to the respiring tissue. Red blood cells are unusual in two main respects:

- They are biconcave in shape. This increases the surface area of the cell, enabling oxygen to diffuse quickly into or out of the cell.
- They have no nucleus. This means there is more room for haemoglobin, maximising the oxygen that can be carried by each cell.

Two views of red blood cells.

White blood cells

White blood cells or leucocytes differ from red blood cells in being larger, possessing a nucleus and being either spherical or irregular in shape.

There are two main groups of white cells:

- Granulocytes, or **macrophages**, have granular cytoplasm and lobed nuclei. Their function is to engulf bacteria by phagocytosis.
- Agranulocytes, or lymphocytes, have clear cytoplasm and spherical nuclei. They produce antibodies and antitoxins.

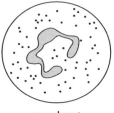

granulocyte   agranulocyte

White blood cells.

Plasma

Plasma is made up of about 90% water. It transports soluble food molecules, waste products, hormones, plasma proteins, mineral ions, vitamins, carbon dioxide, antibodies, etc., and also distributes heat.

Blood groups

Before 1900 attempts to give blood transfusions often proved fatal. It is now known that human blood can be categorised into a variety of blood groups. The ABO system indicates the presence or absence of **agglutinogens** referred to as agglutinogen A and B. The red blood cells of an individual may possess one, both or neither of these **antigens**. This gives four possible blood groups, A, B, AB and O. When a person's blood is identified as blood group A it means they have A antigens on the surface of their red blood cells.

In a person's plasma there are **antibodies** relating to these antigens. The antibodies that a person has are the exact opposite of their blood group. Blood groups are a special example of the antigen–antibody response. Blood groups are inherited.

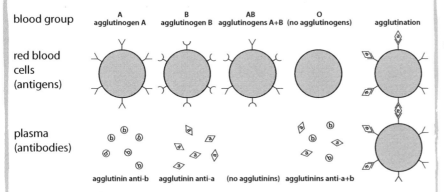

blood group	A agglutinogen A	B agglutinogen B	AB agglutinogens A+B	O (no agglutinogens)	agglutination
red blood cells (antigens)					
plasma (antibodies)	agglutinin anti-b	agglutinin anti-a	(no agglutinins)	agglutinins anti-a+b	

The ABO system of blood grouping.

During a blood transfusion when blood from a donor is added to the blood of the recipient it is necessary to avoid bringing together corresponding antigens and antibodies. For example, antigen A and antibody A must not be mixed since **agglutination** will take place. That is, the red blood cells clump together. These clumps cannot get through the blood vessels.

A person with blood group O contains no antigens on the red blood cells. This blood can be given to all other blood groups. A person with blood group O is said to be an universal donor. But patients of blood group O themselves can receive only group O blood.

Individuals with blood group AB have no antibodies in the blood plasma and can receive blood from group A or group B, as well as group O. A person with group AB blood is said to be a universal recipient.

Key Terms

Agglutinogen = antigen carried on the external surface of the membrane of red blood cells.

Antigen = a molecule that stimulates an immune response by lymphocytes.

Antibody = a protein made by lymphocytes in response to the appropriate antigen.

Agglutination = the clumping of red blood cells.

≫ Pointer

Plasma also contains platelets that are involved in blood clotting. This topic is not included in the specification.

③⑨ Why are people with blood group O called universal donors?

≫ Pointer

When people have a blood transfusion it is important that they receive blood that is compatible with their own blood.

≫ Pointer

Antigens and antibodies are studied in detail on page 92.

≫ Pointer

Transfusion of the wrong blood group into a patient carries the risk of an antigen–antibody reaction leading to agglutination.

Blood transfusions.

Blood group	Can donate blood to	Can receive blood from
A	A and AB	A and O
B	B and AB	B and O
AB	AB	All groups
O	All groups	O

quickfire

(40) Why are people with blood group AB called universal recipients?

Grade boost

People with a protein called the D antigen on their blood cells are said to be RhD positive. People without this antigen are RhD negative.

>> Pointer

A complication can arise during pregnancy if a Rhesus negative female is carrying a Rhesus positive foetus.

quickfire

(41) What treatment is given to a Rhesus negative mother who becomes pregnant with a second Rhesus positive baby?

Grade boost

Consider the symptoms, causes and treatment of anaemia.

quickfire

(42) What are the symptoms of anaemia?

The Rhesus antigen

Another important blood group system is the Rhesus system (RhD system). Red blood cells can also carry the Rhesus antigen which is present in some people (Rh positive) but not in others (Rh negative). Approximately 75% of the human population have this particular antigen on their red blood cells. Unlike the ABO blood groups no-one automatically has anti-Rhesus antibodies in their blood plasma. The antibodies are only produced if some Rhesus positive blood is mixed with Rhesus negative blood. If that happens the blood may agglutinate.

If a Rhesus negative mother is carrying a Rhesus positive baby, a complication can arise with the Rhesus system. (This could happen if the father was Rhesus positive.) As the baby develops in the uterus (womb) the blood of the mother and the baby do not mix, but become very close to each other, in the placenta. Substances such as glucose, oxygen and waste products diffuse between the mother's blood and that of the baby. However, normally the red blood cells are too large to diffuse, but occasionally the baby's red blood cells do manage to pass into the mother's blood. If these cells carry the Rhesus antigen then she will develop Rhesus antibodies against it. This does not normally happen during pregnancy so there is unlikely to be a complication. But during the birth the baby's blood will come in contact with the mother's blood and the mother is said to be sensitised. So if she becomes pregnant with a second Rhesus positive baby, her ready-made anti Rhesus antibodies can diffuse across the placenta and mix with the baby's blood. Here they can cause the baby's red cells to clump together which can be fatal. To ensure this does not happen all pregnant women are tested. A Rhesus negative mother who is carrying a Rhesus positive baby is given an injection of anti-Rhesus antibodies after the birth to destroy any Rhesus positive cells that have entered her circulation. The antibodies given by injection do not persist long as they are soon broken down.

Anaemia

Red blood cells are made in the bone marrow tissue. When first formed the red blood cell has a nucleus but very little haemoglobin. As the cell matures the haemoglobin content increases to 90% of the cell's dry mass. Towards the end of this maturation process the nucleus is squeezed out. Red blood cells have a life-span of about four months. The body needs iron, vitamin B12 and folic acid to produce more red blood cells. If there is a lack of one or more of these, anaemia will develop.

Haemoglobin has a high affinity for oxygen and combines readily with it to form oxyhaemoglobin. It is in this form that oxygen is carried from regions of high oxygen tension (lungs) to regions of low oxygen tension (respiring tissues). If there is a shortage of red blood cells or haemoglobin the body is starved of oxygen. This lack of oxygen is responsible for the symptoms of the condition called anaemia. Some people are anaemic but do not show symptoms for months. When symptoms do appear they include tiredness, feeling weak, sometimes having dizzy spells and feeling faint. As the condition becomes more severe additional symptoms include shortness of breath, palpitations and headaches. In addition the patient looks pale.

Anyone can suffer with anaemia. Most often it affects females of childbearing age, men and women over 75, growing children and teenagers. 'Iron deficiency anaemia' is the most common type of anaemia. In the UK 8% of women have this type of anaemia.

Common causes of anaemia happening slowly over time are a lack of iron in the diet, failure to absorb iron, or through excessive bleeding when a female has heavy periods. Anaemia can also happen suddenly, for example when a stomach ulcer bursts. Anaemia can also be an inherited condition.

A person suspected of being anaemic will have a blood sample taken. This will be sent to a hospital pathology laboratory where a blood cell count will be measured. Normally, one would expect to find that there are about 5.2 million red blood cells per mm^3 in a male adult and 4.8 million red cells per mm^3 in a female. If it is found that the red blood cell count is below normal, the treatment will depend on the cause of the anaemia. If due to lack of iron, iron (ferrous sulphate) tablets are usually prescribed. Dietary advice is also given to encourage the patient to eat iron-rich foods, such as red meat, eggs, milk, spinach, etc., to speed the process of building up iron in the body. It is also important to have a plentiful supply of vitamin C in the diet because it is thought to help the body absorb iron. When the anaemia is more severe a blood transfusion may be necessary.

43 Name three foods that are rich in iron.

44 What is the treatment for severe anaemia?

The circulatory system

All mammals have a double circulatory system. This means that the blood passes twice through the heart for each complete circuit of the body. When blood is passed to the lungs, its pressure is reduced. If the blood were to pass from the lungs directly to the rest of the body its pressure would make the circulation very slow. Instead the blood is returned to the heart before being pumped to the rest of the body. Materials are then delivered quickly to the body cells to meet metabolic demands.

The double circulatory system may be described as follows:

- The pulmonary circulation – the right side of the heart pumps deoxygenated blood to the lungs. Oxygenated blood then returns to the left side of the heart.

- Systemic circulation – the left side of the heart pumps the oxygenated blood to the tissues. Deoxygenated blood then returns to the right side of the heart.

> **Pointer**
> Arteries and veins transport materials whereas gaseous exchange takes place in the capillaries.

> **Pointer**
> Arteries carry blood away from the heart, veins carry blood to the heart.

> **Pointer**
> In each circuit the blood passes through the heart twice, once through the right side and once through the left side.

Structure and function of blood vessels

There are three types of blood vessels: arteries, veins and capillaries. Arteries and veins have the same basic three-layered structure but the proportions of the different layers vary.

In both arteries and veins:

- The innermost layer is the endothelium, which is one cell thick and provides a smooth lining to reduce friction and provide a minimum resistance to the flow of the blood.
- The middle layer is made up of elastic fibres and smooth muscle. This layer is thicker in the arteries than in the veins to accommodate changes in blood flow and pressure as blood is pumped from the heart.
- The outer layer is made up of collagen fibres which are resistant to over-stretching.

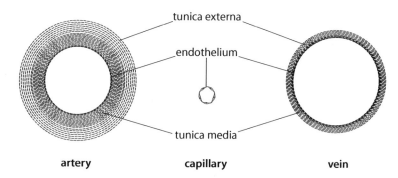

Artery, capillary and vein.

Arteries carry blood away from the heart. The arteries have thick, muscular walls to withstand the high pressure of blood received from the heart. The contraction of the arterial muscles also helps to maintain pressure as the blood is transported further from the heart.

The arteries branch into smaller vessels called arterioles that further subdivide into thin-walled capillaries. The capillaries form a vast network which penetrates all the tissues and organs of the body. Blood from the capillaries collects into venules, which in turn empty blood into veins, from which it is returned to the heart.

Veins have semi-lunar valves along their length to ensure flow in one direction (prevent backflow); these are not present in arteries apart from the aortic valves.

The capillaries are thin walled consisting only of a layer of endothelium so their walls are permeable to water and dissolved substances such as glucose. It is at the capillaries that the exchange of materials between the blood and the tissues takes place.

Capillaries have a small diameter, and friction with the walls slows the blood flow. Although the diameter is small, there are many capillaries in the capillary bed providing a large total cross-sectional area which further reduces blood flow. This low velocity in very thin-walled vessels enhances their ability to exchange materials with the surrounding tissue fluid.

Grade boost

You will be expected to relate the structure of the blood vessels to their functions.

Grade boost

Construct a table comparing an artery and a vein. In an exam question it is important to make a true comparison. It is insufficient to state that veins have a large lumen without adding that arteries have a small lumen.

quickpire

45 Give two reasons why arteries have a thick muscular wall.

Grade boost

Capillaries are numerous and highly branched providing a large surface area for diffusion.

» Pointer

It may at first seem that the blood should travel faster through capillaries than through arteries, because the diameters of the capillaries are much smaller. However, it is the total cross-sectional area delivering the blood that determines the flow rate.

quickpire

46 The capillaries slow down the flow of blood at the tissues. What is the significance of this?

The heart

A pump to circulate blood is an essential feature of a circulatory system. The heart consists of a relatively thin-walled collection chamber and a thick-walled pumping chamber which are partitioned into two, allowing the complete separation of oxygenated and deoxygenated blood. The heart is really two separate pumps lying side by side. The pump on the left deals with oxygenated blood and that on the right deals with deoxygenated blood. Each pump has two chambers, the upper atrium and the lower ventricle.

The four-chambered heart consists largely of cardiac muscle, a specialised tissue that is capable of rhythmical contraction and relaxation of its own accord throughout a person's life. The heart muscle is said to be **myogenic**.

Key Terms

Myogenic = the heartbeat is initiated from within the muscle itself and not due to nerve stimulation.

Systole = stage in which the heart muscle contracts.

Diastole = stage in which the heart muscle relaxes.

> **Pointer**
> You are required to name only the main blood vessels associated with the heart.

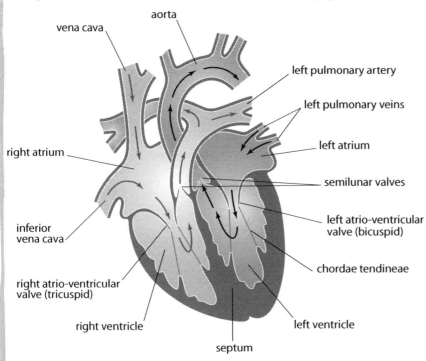

Heart.

Cardiac cycle

The cardiac cycle describes the sequence of events in one heartbeat. The pumping action of the heart consists of alternating contractions (**systole**) and relaxations (**diastole**).

There are three stages to the cardiac cycle.

Atrial systole

The right and left ventricles relax, the tricuspid and bicuspid valves open as the atria contract and blood flows into the ventricles.

Ventricular systole

The atria relax and the right and left ventricles contract together forcing blood out of the heart into the pulmonary artery and the aorta as the semilunar valves are opened. The tricuspid and bicuspid valves are closed by the rise in ventricular

> **Pointer**
> Be careful not to confuse systole and diastole.

pressure. The pulmonary artery carries deoxygenated blood to the lungs and the aorta carries oxygenated blood to the various parts of the body.

Diastole

The ventricles relax and the pressure in the ventricles falls. Blood under high pressure in the arteries causes the semilunar valves to shut, preventing blood from going back into the ventricles. Blood from the vena cava and pulmonary veins enters the atria and the cycle starts again.

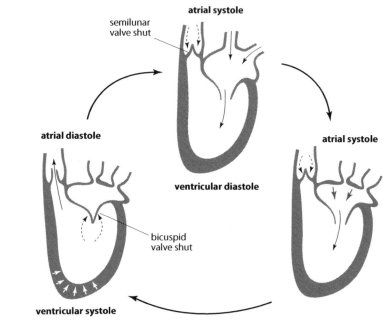

Cardiac cycle .

The following describes the flow of blood through the left side of the heart. The left atrium is relaxed and receives oxygenated blood from the pulmonary vein. When full, the pressure forces open the bicuspid valve between the atrium and ventricle. Relaxation of the left ventricle draws blood from the left atrium. The left atrium contracts, pushing the remaining blood into the left ventricle through the valve. With the left atrium relaxed and with the bicuspid valve closed the left ventricle contracts. The strong muscular walls exert a strong pressure and push blood away from the heart through the semilunar valves through the pulmonary arteries and the aorta.

- Both sides of the heart work together. Both ventricles contract at the same time, both atria contract together. One complete contraction and relaxation is called a heartbeat.
- After contraction, when the compartment has been emptied of blood, it relaxes, to be filled with blood once more.
- The ventricles contain more muscle than the atria and so generate more pressure to force the blood a greater distance.
- The left ventricle has a thicker muscular wall than the right ventricle as it has to pump the blood all round the body, whereas the right ventricle has only to pump the blood a shorter distance to the lungs.

>> Pointer

Don't confuse the cardiac cycle with the control of heartbeat.

>> Pointer

Relate the opening and closing of valves to the pumping action of the heart.

(47) Why does the left ventricle have a thicker muscular wall than the right ventricle?

Valves

Valves are used to prevent any unwanted backflow of blood. Whether the valves are the atrio-ventricular valves (bicuspid and tricuspid), semi-lunar valves, or the valves in veins, they have the same design and operate in the same way.

Pressure changes in the heart

- The highest pressure occurs in the aorta/arteries that show a rhythmic rise and fall corresponding to ventricular contraction.

- Friction with vessel walls causes a progressive drop in pressure. Arterioles have a large total surface area and a relatively narrow bore causing a substantial reduction from aortic pressure. Their pressure depends on whether they are dilated or contracted.

- The extensive capillary beds have a large cross-sectional area. These beds create an even greater resistance to blood flow.

- There is a relationship between pressure and speed and the pressure drops further due to leakage from capillaries into tissues.

- The return flow to the heart is non-rhythmic and the pressure in the veins is low but can be increased by the massaging effect of muscles.

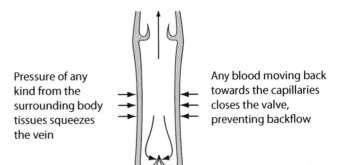

Pressure of any kind from the surrounding body tissues squeezes the vein

Any blood moving back towards the capillaries closes the valve, preventing backflow

How a valve functions in a vein.

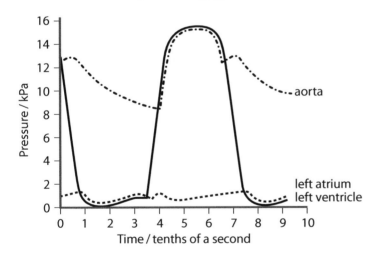

Changes in pressure.

Control of heartbeat

- Cardiac muscle is myogenic.

- Within the wall of the right atrium is a region of specialised cardiac fibres called the sinoatrial node (SAN) which acts as a pacemaker.

- A wave of electrical stimulation arises at this point and then spreads over the two atria causing them to contract more or less at the same time.

≫ Pointer

The graphical analysis of pressure changes in the heart is a favourite exam question. Be prepared to describe the pressure changes involved in the flow of blood from one chamber of the heart to another together with the associated opening and closing of the valves.

- The electrical stimulation is prevented from spreading to the ventricles by a thin layer of connective tissue. This acts as a layer of insulation (it is important that the muscles of the ventricles do not start to contract until the muscles of the atria have finished contracting).
- The stimulation reaches another specialised region of cardiac fibres, the atrio-ventricular node (AVN), which lies between the two atria and which passes on the excitation to specialised tissues in the ventricles.
- From the AVN the excitation passes down the bundle of His to the apex. The bundle branches into Purkinje fibres in the ventricle walls which carry the wave of excitation upwards through the ventricle muscle.
- The impulses cause the cardiac muscle in each ventricle to contract simultaneously from the apex upwards.
- This ensures that the ventricles are emptied completely.

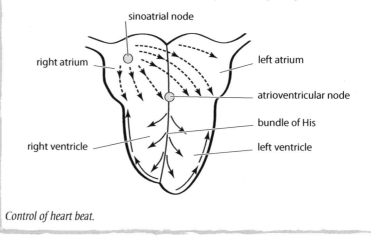

Control of heart beat.

Monitoring circulation

A number of different methods of measurement are used in monitoring circulation to determine health and fitness.

Measuring pulse rate

Ventricular contraction (systole) sends a wave of blood through the arteries. Each time the heart contracts it forces blood out into the aorta and pulmonary arteries. The surge of blood from each heartbeat causes a bulge in the walls of the arteries and this elastic recoil of the artery wall can be felt as a pulse, particularly where the artery is near the skin surface and passes over a bone. The pulse is usually taken on the underside of the wrist. One pulse is equivalent to one heartbeat. Thus, the pulse rate is the same as the heart rate.

The resting pulse rate gives a good indication of a person's fitness. The fitter an individual is, the lower their pulse rate. A lower pulse rate means that the same volume of blood is being passed out of the heart per minute but with fewer heartbeats. The normal resting pulse rate for a person is between 60 and 100 beats per minute, with the average pulse rate for a healthy, fit young adult being about 70.

Physically fit individuals tend to pump out a greater volume of blood with each heartbeat; therefore the heart does not have to beat as quickly during exercise. Also, when the exercise is over, their pulse rate returns to normal far more quickly than with unfit people.

Measuring blood pressure

There are alternate contractions (systole) and relaxations (diastole) of the heart. Two different pressures are normally measured:

- Systolic blood pressure is the maximum pressure produced in the left ventricle during systole.
- Diastolic blood pressure is the minimum blood pressure in the aorta.

The picture shows a sphygmomanometer, an instrument used to measure blood pressure.

Blood pressure for young, healthy adults is around 120/75. An individual with a persistently high diastolic pressure at rest is said to be suffering from hypertension or high blood pressure. An individual with long-term hypertension has an increased risk of suffering a heart attack and **stroke**.

Diastole is when the ventricles relax and at this time the pressure inside the left ventricle drops below that in the arteries. Diastolic pressure gives an indication of the resistance of the arteries to the flow of blood. If the resistance is low then the diastolic pressure is low but if the resistance to blood flow is high, then the diastolic pressure will be high.

Factors such as diet and smoking increase the resistance to blood flow. Thus the heart has to work harder to pump the blood to the tissues. The risk of high blood pressure increases with age. In the UK 25% of the population over 55 are suffering from hypertension.

Table showing average blood pressure changes with age.

Age (years)	Average systolic pressure/mmHg	Average diastolic pressure/mmHg
baby	80	46
20	120	80
60	135	89
60 with hypertension	160	110

A healthy artery has a pale, smooth lining, but in an unhealthy artery there are yellow, fatty streaks under the endothelium. A fat deposit, called an atheroma, built up from cholesterol taken up from the blood, causes the lumen, through which blood flows, to become much narrower and also lessens the elasticity of the artery wall. The build-up of material increases the resistance to blood flow. This condition is called atherosclerosis. If it occurs in a coronary artery, a pain (called angina) is experienced during exercise.

Key Term

Stroke = damage to the brain caused by a blood clot carried in the blood getting stuck in an artery supplying blood to the brain.

Grade boost

A persistently high diastolic pressure in a person at rest is known as hypertension. There is an increased risk of suffering a heart attack and stroke with long-term hypertension.

Using a sphygmomanometer to measure blood pressure.

Pointer

You would not be expected to describe how to use a sphygmomanometer.

Grade boost

Many factors, inherited and environmental, will affect pulse rate. Blood pressure values are averages.

Atherosclerosis increases the risk of a blood clot forming in the artery. If this happens in a coronary artery it is known as a coronary thrombosis. If blood is prevented from passing through a coronary artery the heart muscle it supplies may stop beating. This is called a **myocardial infarction** or heart attack.

Hypertension in an individual can be reduced by having a healthy diet, taking regular exercise, avoiding stress and not smoking. If it persists, despite a change in lifestyle, drugs are prescribed until the condition is under control.

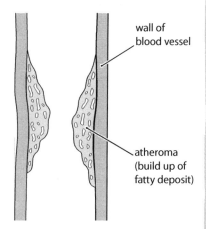

Artery showing an atheroma.

Electrocardiogram

The electrical activity taking place in the heart as it beats can be measured using an electrocardiogram (ECG). It is a quick and important means of collecting information to diagnose problems affecting the heart. Electrodes are attached to the patient's chest and the electrical activity is displayed as an electrocardiograph by means of a chart recorder. The ECG shows the electrical activity that takes place in the heart muscle as the heart beats. The activity is related to the electrical impulses that pass through the heart.

The graph shows how the different parts of the ECG correspond to the pressure changes during one heartbeat. The P wave corresponds to atrial contraction, the QRS wave comes immediately before the contraction of the ventricles, and the T wave represents the relaxation of the ventricles.

How a normal ECG relates to the cardiac cycle.

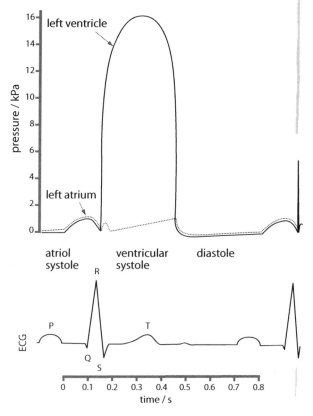

Table summarising how electrical impulses move through the heart.

Cardiac control	Action of heart muscle	Electrocardiogram activity
SAN impulse	Atrial wall contracts	P wave
AVN	Delay	
Purkinje tissue	Ventricle contracts from base	QRS wave
	Ventricles relax	T wave

A variety of cardiac disorders can produce irregularities in this activity. The resultant electrocardiogram trace can be compared with a normal ECG with its characteristic P wave, QRS wave and T wave.

The ECG traces shown below are those of patients each with one of three forms of **arrhythmia**:

- Ventricular fibrillation – the ECG shows no pattern, the contractions of the heart are very irregular. Diagnosis is a heart attack.

- Heart block – where the atria and ventricles are beating independently and there is a much longer time interval between the P and R 'peaks'. This could be because the Purkinje fibres are damaged. There are several degrees of heart block with the more serious form requiring the fitting of a 'pacemaker'.

- Atrial fibrillation – where the atria beat rapidly and in an irregular way. It may cause no symptoms, but it is often associated with palpitations, fainting and chest pain. The normal regular electrical impulses generated by the sinoatrial node are overwhelmed by disorganised electrical impulses usually originating in the roots of the pulmonary veins, leading to irregular conduction of impulses to the ventricles which generate the heartbeat. Rate control may be achieved with medication.

Types of arrhythmia.

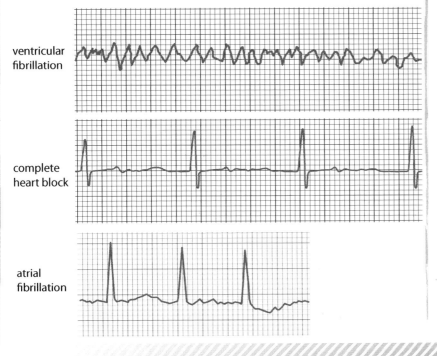

Key Term

Arrhythmia = a deviation or disturbance of the normal heart rhythm.

》 Pointer

An electrocardiogram (ECG) shows the electrical activity which takes place in the heart muscle as the heart beats.

quickfire

㊾ What happens to the ventricles immediately after the QRS 'spike'?

Grade boost

Relate the ECG waves with the pressure changes in the heart.
Note that the ECG waves happen before the pressure changes.

》 Pointer

Refer back to the control of heartbeat on page 79.

Treatment of heart disease

Grade boost

Research the advantages and disadvantages of angioplasty, coronary bypass surgery and heart transplant surgery for the treatment of severe heart disease.

» Pointer

Heart transplant patients have to be treated with immunosuppressant drugs throughout their lives.

quickpire

(54) Explain the principle of the technique of angioplasty.

quickpire

(55) How does angioplasty relieve angina?

Lifestyle changes may not solve the underlying problem of heart disease.

A heart attack is a very dangerous event. If an individual has angina or other symptoms of heart disease, everything possible should be done to improve the health of their heart and blood supply. Reducing body weight and taking regular exercise are both very beneficial. A patient may be helped by changing their diet. For some people these changes in lifestyle help to prevent further deterioration of their coronary arteries. High risk patients may be prescribed aspirin which is taken as a daily dose, usually 75 mg per day. Aspirin or warfarin reduces the ability of blood to clot. Many people who are at risk from coronary thrombosis take aspirin on a regular basis.

A heart attack occurs when there is a sudden and severe blockage of the coronary artery. A person suffering a heart attack is given 'clot bursting drugs', such as streptokinase, ideally within the first hour after the onset of the attack. If the condition becomes severe and affects the quality of life it may be necessary to perform heart surgery. This can be carried out in a number of different ways.

Angioplasty is a surgical technique which does not involve opening the chest cavity. It may be used to improve the health of a patient suffering from angina and for whom other treatments have not been successful. It is also used for patients who have had bypass surgery and whose coronary vessels need to be widened again. Angioplasty is a less invasive procedure than open heart surgery. The patient is given a general anaesthetic then a small balloon is threaded into the partly blocked coronary artery though a tube. It is then inflated and as the balloon expands it presses against the atheroma and makes one or two tears in it. This allows the artery wall to be pushed outwards by the pressure of the blood, restoring the lumen to something like its normal width. The balloon is deflated and removed.

Many heart operations involve 'open-heart' surgery where the chest cavity is cut open to expose the heart. Coronary bypass surgery is used when a patient's coronary arteries are so badly blocked that insufficient blood can pass through them to supply the heart muscle with oxygen. The 'bypass' is an extra blood vessel which provides an alternate route for the blood to the heart wall, bypassing the coronary arteries. A piece of the aorta artery or vein is taken, often from the leg, and the introduced blood vessel is stitched to the aorta at one end and to a coronary artery at the other. It is a very delicate procedure and the surgeon cannot carry out the operation while the heart is beating. It is therefore necessary to employ a heart-lung machine to pump the blood around the body during open-heart surgery.

The transport of gases

The transport of oxygen

To be efficient at transporting oxygen, haemoglobin needs to readily associate with oxygen at the surface where gas exchange is taking place, the lungs, and readily dissociate from oxygen at those tissues, such as muscle, that require it. Haemoglobin is a remarkable molecule that is able to carry out these seemingly contradictory requirements. It is able to change its **affinity** for oxygen in the presence of carbon dioxide by changing its shape. The altered shape binds more loosely with oxygen and releases it.

When a pigment is exposed to increasing **partial pressures of oxygen** it would be expected that it would absorb oxygen evenly and the graph plotted would be a straight line bisecting the two axes.

When the respiratory pigment haemoglobin is exposed to a gradual increase in oxygen tension it absorbs oxygen rapidly at first but more slowly as the tension continues to rise. This relationship is known as the oxygen dissociation curve.

At very low concentrations it is difficult for haemoglobin to absorb oxygen but once loaded it associates readily with oxygen. At high partial pressures of oxygen, the percentage saturation of oxygen is very high.

Red blood cells load oxygen in the lungs where the partial pressure is high and the haemoglobin becomes saturated with oxygen. The cells carry the oxygen as oxyhaemoglobin to the respiring tissues, e.g. muscle, where the partial pressure is low (as oxygen is being used up in respiration to create energy). Oxyhaemoglobin then unloads its oxygen, that is, it dissociates.

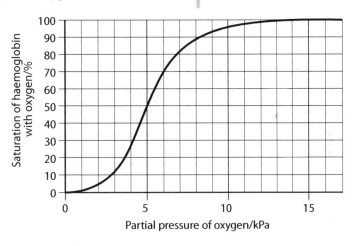

Graph of oxygen dissociation

The graph also shows that a very small decrease in the partial pressure of oxygen leads to a considerable amount of oxygen becoming dissociated from haemoglobin.

Two facts are important to bear in mind:

- The more the dissociation curve of haemoglobin is displaced to the left, the more readily it picks up oxygen, but the less readily it releases it.
- The more the dissociation curve of haemoglobin is displaced to the right, the less readily it picks up oxygen, but the more easily it releases it.

Key Terms

Affinity = one molecule having a chemical attraction for another.

Partial pressure (of oxygen (pO$_2$)) = normal atmospheric pressure is 100 kPa. As oxygen makes up 21% of the atmosphere its maximum partial pressure is 21 kPa.

Grade boost

The oxygen dissociation curve is a difficult concept so study it thoroughly.

Pointer

When referring to the combination of oxygen with haemoglobin, use the terms loading or associating; and when referring to haemoglobin releasing its oxygen, use the terms unloading or dissociating.

quickfire

56 In what form is oxygen transported in the blood?

Key Term

Bohr effect = the higher the partial pressure of carbon dioxide the more the curve shifts to the right.

The effects of carbon dioxide concentration

At higher partial pressure of carbon dioxide the oxygen dissociation curve shifts to the right. This phenomenon is known as the **Bohr effect**. When oxygen reaches respiring tissues, such as muscle, the high partial pressure of carbon dioxide there enables haemoglobin to unload its oxygen even more readily.

- The release of oxygen from haemoglobin is facilitated by the presence of carbon dioxide. When the partial pressure of oxygen is high, as in the lung capillaries, oxygen combines with the haemoglobin to form oxyhaemoglobin.

- When the partial pressure of oxygen is low, as found in the respiring tissues, then the oxygen dissociates from the haemoglobin.

- When the partial pressure of carbon dioxide is high, haemoglobin is less efficient at associating with oxygen and more efficient at releasing it.

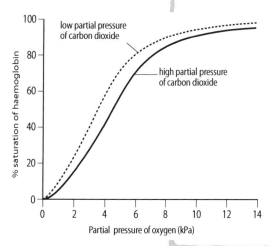

Graph showing Bohr effect.

》》Pointer

The Bohr effect is concerned with the uptake of oxygen by haemoglobin at low partial pressures and the offloading of oxygen at the tissues as a result of the high levels of carbon dioxide there.

quickfire

㊄ Explain the significance of the difference between the oxygen dissociation curve of a foetus and the mother.

Grade boost

Haemoglobin has a reduced affinity for oxygen in the presence of carbon dioxide.

》》Pointer

Myoglobin acts as an oxygen store in muscle.

The dissociation curve of foetal haemoglobin

The blood of the foetus and the mother flow closely together in the placenta but rarely mix. To enable the foetal haemoglobin to absorb oxygen from the maternal haemoglobin in the placenta the foetus has a haemoglobin that differs (in two of the four polypeptide chains) from the haemoglobin of the adult. This structural difference makes the foetal haemoglobin dissociation curve shift to the left of that of the adult. The foetal haemoglobin combines with oxygen more readily than does the mother's haemoglobin. That is, the foetal haemoglobin has a greater affinity for oxygen.

Myoglobin

Normally, the respiring muscle obtains its oxygen from haemoglobin. However, if the oxygen partial pressure becomes very low, as when exercising, oxymyoglobin unloads its oxygen. The oxygen held by the myoglobin acts as a reserve, to be used only in conditions of particular oxygen demand, such as sustained activity.

Myoglobin is far more stable than haemoglobin and will not release its oxygen unless the partial pressure of oxygen is extremely low. The dissociation curve of myoglobin is far to the left of that of haemoglobin. At each partial pressure of oxygen, myoglobin has a higher percentage oxygen saturation than haemoglobin.

The transport of carbon dioxide

Carbon dioxide is transported in blood cells and plasma in three ways:

- In solution in the plasma (5%).
- As hydrogen carbonate (85%).
- In combination with haemoglobin to form carbamino-haemoglobin (10%). ·

Some carbon dioxide is transported in the red blood cells but most is converted in the red blood cells to hydrogen carbonate, which is then dissolved in the plasma.

The following describes a series of reactions known as the chloride shift:

- Carbon dioxide diffuses into the red blood cell (RBC) and combines with water to form carbonic acid. The reaction is catalysed by carbonic anhydrase.
- Carbonic acid dissociates into H^+ and HCO_3^- ions. HCO_3^- ions diffuse out of the RBC into the plasma where they combine with Na^+ ions from the dissociation of sodium chloride to form sodium hydrogen carbonate.
- H^+ ions provide the conditions for the oxyhaemoglobin to dissociate into oxygen and haemoglobin.
- H^+ ions are buffered by their combination with haemoglobin and the formation of haemoglobinic acid (HHb).
- The oxygen diffuses out of the RBC into the tissues.
- To balance the outward movement of negatively charged ions, chloride ions diffuse in.
- It is by this means that the electrochemical neutrality of the RBC is maintained.

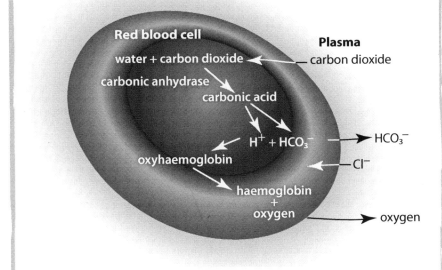

Summary of chloride shift.

》 Pointer

Some carbon dioxide is transported in the red blood cells but most is converted in the red blood cells to bicarbonate which is then dissolved in the plasma. The chloride shift refers to the influx of chloride ions into the red blood cells to preserve electrical neutrality.

≪ Grade boost

Haemoglobin acts as a buffer helping to maintain the blood pH by removing hydrogen ions from solution.

58 What is the significance of the inward movement of chloride ions to the red blood cell?

Key Term

Tissue fluid = plasma minus plasma proteins.

Intercellular fluid

The capillaries are the site of exchange between the blood and the cells of the body. They are well adapted to allow the exchange of materials between the blood and the cells.

- They have thin, permeable walls.
- They provide a large surface area for exchange of materials.
- Blood flows very slowly through the capillaries allowing time for exchange of materials.

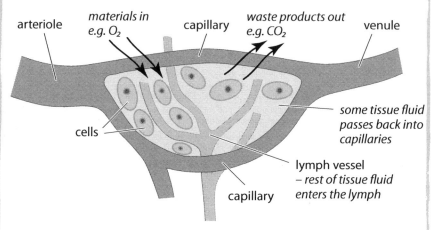

Diagram showing a capillary network.

Blood consists of the fluid plasma that carries the blood cells, dissolved materials and large molecules, called plasma proteins. The blood is contained in a closed system but fluid from the plasma escapes through the walls of the capillaries. This fluid is called **tissue fluid** and bathes the cells, supplying them with glucose, amino acids, fatty acids, salts and oxygen. The tissue fluid also removes waste materials from the cells.

When blood reaches the arterial end of a capillary it is under pressure because of the pumping action of the heart and the resistance to blood flow of the capillaries. This hydrostatic pressure forces the fluid part of the blood through the capillary walls into the spaces between the cells.

This outward flow is opposed by the reduced water potential of the blood, created by the presence of the plasma proteins. The hydrostatic pressure of the blood is greater than the osmotic forces so there is a net flow of water and solutes out of the blood. At the arterial end of the capillary bed the diffusion gradient for solutes such as glucose, oxygen and ions favours movement from the capillaries to the tissue fluid. This is because these substances are being used during cell metabolism.

59 Name the two opposing forces involved in forcing tissue fluid out of the blood plasma in capillaries and into the surrounding tissues.

At the venous end of the capillary bed the blood pressure is lower and water passes into the capillaries by osmosis. The reduced water potential of the blood created by the presence of the plasma proteins causes a net inflow of water.

At the venous end tissue fluid picks up CO_2 and other excretory substances. Some of this fluid passes back into the capillaries, but some drains into the **lymphatic system** and is returned eventually to the venous system via the thoracic duct, which empties into a vein near the heart.

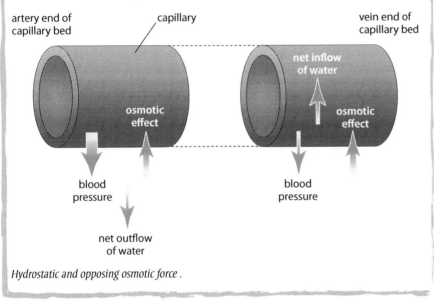

Hydrostatic and opposing osmotic force .

Kwashiorkor

Low blood proteins affect capillary filtration and may result in fluid retention in tissues. Receiving the right amount of protein is a particular problem in those parts of the world with large populations and where livestock is scarce. The diet of many native Africans consists largely of cornmeal, which does not provide some of the essential amino acids. As a result many African children develop a protein deficiency disorder called kwashiorkor, one of the symptoms of which is oedema. This is a condition where tissue fluid is formed faster than it can be removed. Fluid accumulates in the tissues and the tissues swell up. A child suffering from kwashiorkor is also physically weak and shows retarded growth.

Grade boost

Non-specific mechanisms
do not distinguish between
one type of pathogen and
another, whereas specific
mechanisms do distinguish
between different pathogens.

Grade boost

Be prepared to link relevant
parts of the specification. For
example, the low pH in the
stomach means that most
pathogens are killed in that
region.

>>> Pointer

Over-use of wide spectrum
bacteria can destroy natural
skin flora bacteria.

⊙◄◄◄◄ quickfire

62 State two ways in which
healthy undamaged skin
protects the body against
invading pathogens.

Human defence mechanisms

The body has a number of lines of defence against **disease**:

- Physical barriers, such as the skin, keep harmful micro-organisms (pathogens) from entering the body.
- The process of phagocytosis.
- The immune response – once a pathogen has been identified, a specific response from white blood cells (lymphocytes) takes place.

Defence mechanisms may be divided into two types, non-specific and specific.

Non-specific mechanisms

- Natural barriers such as the skin, skin flora and blood clotting to seal wounds. Additional protection is provided by ciliated mucus membranes, lysozyme enzyme and stomach acid.
- Resistance to disease depends on the general health and diet. For instance, a deficiency of vitamin C leads to weakened connective tissue causing open wounds.
- The skin flora (a natural population of harmless micro-organisms that live on the skin surface) protect by competing with pathogenic bacteria for nutrients.
- Localised defence involves inflammation and phagocytosis.

Inflammation

Damage to the body's tissues triggers a defence response called inflammation. The symptoms include pain, redness, heat and swelling. Inflammation has three functions:

- It destroys the cause of the infection.
- It confines the infection to a small area limiting the effects on the body.
- It replaces or repairs damaged tissue.

If an individual is cut and there are bacteria on the offending object, the defence process occurs in three stages:

1. There is an increase in diameter and permeability of the blood vessels in the damaged area. This increases blood flow and allows defence cells to reach the area. Blood clots form in damaged blood vessels.
2. Within about an hour white blood cells, called phagocytes, arrive and start to destroy invading microbes. They do so by engulfing the microbes. After a few days an abscess starts to form. This consists of dead phagocytes, damaged tissue and various body fluids, collectively called pus.
3. New cells replace damaged tissue.

Skin wound in section.

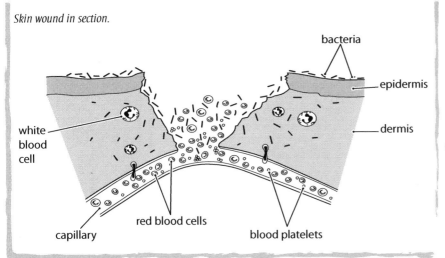

quickfire

⑥③ Name the organelle which releases enzymes to break down pathogens.

》 Pointer

The response of specific mechanisms is slower but provides long-lasting **immunity**.

Grade boost

Lymphocytes are formed from stem cells found in the bone marrow.

》 Pointer

White blood cells are studied on page 72.

Phagocytosis

White blood cells called phagocytes provide an important defence against pathogens by engulfing them in vesicles. The process takes place as follows.

A phagocyte moves towards a bacterium and attaches itself to its surface. It engulfs the bacterium to form a vesicle. Lysosomes move towards the vesicle, fuse with it and enzymes from within the vesicle digest the pathogen. The soluble products are absorbed into the phagocyte.

① Phagocytosis of enemy cell (antigen)

② Fusion of lysosome and enemy cell

③ Enzymes start to degrade enemy cell

④ Enemy cell broken into small fragments

⑤ Fragments of antigen presented on APC surface

⑥ Leftover fragments released by exocytosis

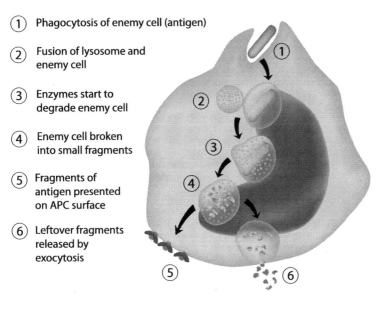

Summary of phagocytosis.

>> *Pointer*

The antibody–antigen reaction is studied in more detail on page 94.

(64) To which special group of blood proteins do antibodies belong?

Grade boost

Be prepared to explain how the antibody is able to attach to a specific antigen.

Specific mechanisms

If the pathogens have got past the first line of defence, specific responses react to individual forms of infection. These responses involve white blood cells called lymphocytes. The responses are of two types: cell-mediated responses involving T lymphocytes and humoral responses involving B lymphocytes.

In order to understand the immune response it is important to distinguish between the terms antigen and antibody:

- An antigen is any substance that when introduced into the blood or tissues triggers the formation of antibodies, or reacts with them if they are already present. Antigens are normally large, complex molecules such as proteins and other polymers. Antigens are called self-antigens if they occur on the surface of cells in the body and non-self if they are from 'foreign' organisms. The presence of a non-self antigen triggers the production of an antibody.

- Antibodies are glycoproteins that belong to a group of blood proteins called immunoglobulins. The basic structure of an antibody consists of a Y-shaped molecule made up from a large pair and a small pair of polypeptide chains. Each antibody has two identical antigen-binding sites. This is different for each kind of antibody and is therefore called the variable region. This allows the antibody to recognise and attach specifically to a particular antigen. Antibodies are produced by lymphocytes in the presence of a specific antigen that can combine with that antigen to neutralise, inhibit or destroy it. That is, each antibody is specific for a particular antigen and reacts with it rendering it harmless.

Antibody.

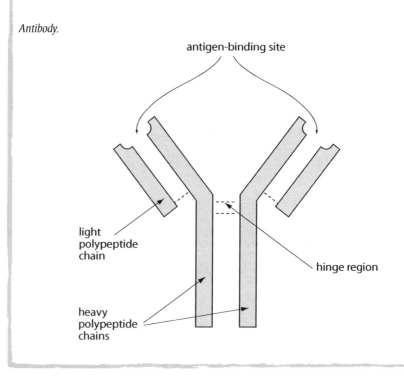

Cell-mediated immune response

This response involves T lymphocytes (T cells). There are millions of types of T lymphocytes, each capable of recognising and attacking a particular type of antigen. The thymus gland (a lymph gland in the neck) is active from birth until a mammal is weaned. During this time it causes lymphocytes to mature and become 'immunologically competent', and capable of synthesising new receptor molecules and incorporating them into the plasma membrane. T lymphocytes leave the thymus and circulate in the blood and body fluids.

Cell-mediated immunity takes place as follows:

- Macrophages engulf pathogens having non-self antigens on their surface and the macrophages 'present' these antigens on their own membranes.

- Binding sites on the surface of specific T lymphocytes recognise and fit with the antigen.

- The T lymphocytes are triggered and start to multiply rapidly. They divide by mitosis and produce a large clone of identical cells, all of which recognise the antigen as being non-self.

- Each cell in the clone can attach to a complementary antigen and destroy it.

- This clone differentiates into the following cell types:

  - T killer cells destroy the antigens directly by attaching to them by lysis, e.g. they destroy virus-infected or cancer cells.

  - Helper T cells which activate B lymphocytes to initiate an antibody response.

  - T suppressor cells suppress other cells in the immune system, e.g. by turning off antibody production when the antigen is no longer present.

  - **Memory cells** show no immediate action but multiply rapidly if the antigen invades for a second time producing an even larger clone of T lymphocytes, and a more rapid destruction of the antigen.

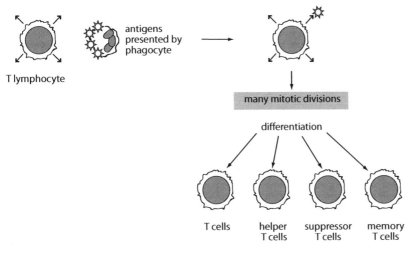

Role of T cells in cell-mediated immunity.

Pointer

The first stage of specific response to infection, described on page 93, is the build-up of the numbers of T cells. Some of these cells produce factors which stimulate B cells to divide.

 Grade boost

There are many thousands of different types of B cells each type producing a different antibody that responds to one specific antigen.

Pointer

The humoral immune response is also known as antibody-mediated response.

Grade boost

Humoral immunity is most effective against bacteria whereas cell-mediated immunity is most effective against viruses.

Grade boost

Antibodies have a binding site that fits precisely on to the antigen to form an antigen–antibody complex.

Humoral immune response

This response involves B lymphocytes (B cells). The B lymphocytes attack and destroy the antigen on the surface of micro-organisms and other foreign (non-self) material by producing antibodies that circulate in the blood and tissue fluid. There are many thousands of different B lymphocytes; each has different immunoglobulins on its cell surface.

Humoral immune response takes place as follows:

- Antigens embedded in the cell membrane of a macrophage are recognised by B lymphocytes.
- B lymphocytes are triggered when specific binding sites on their surface membrane attach to the antigens.
- The activated cells divide rapidly by mitosis forming a clone of plasma cells in the lymph node. Most of these cells produce antibodies but some produce memory cells.
- The antibodies circulate and bind with the specific antigen and destroy it. Plasma cells are responsible for the immediate defence against infection. This is known as the primary immune response.
- The plasma cells live only a few days but can synthesise and secrete vast quantities of specific antibody molecules. The memory cells persist for a long time, sometimes for life. They confer active immunity against the specific antigen. If that antigen is encountered again, the memory cells can recognise it and stimulate the immediate production of massive quantities of antibody. This is called the secondary immune response.

Antibodies and antigens

The antibody becomes attached to the antigen at the antigen-binding site. This causes the antibody to change from a T shape to a Y shape. This exposes part of the antibody molecule to substances in the blood plasma. The process of destroying bacteria takes place as follows:

- B lymphocytes recognise antigens on the surface of bacteria as non-self and produce antibodies against them.
- Antibodies and antigens form immune complexes on the bacterial surface making the bacteria clump together.
- Phagocytic white blood cells engulf bacteria beginning the process of phagocytosis.
- Phagocytes destroy the engulfed bacteria which have been attacked by antibodies.
- Phagocytosis is complete and the destroyed bacteria are contained in a vacuole within the phagocyte.

Types of immunity

The type of immunity described previously involving B lymphocytes and T lymphocytes is called active immunity because the lymphocytes are activated by antigens present on the surface of the pathogen. Since the activation takes place during the natural course of an infection it is called natural active immunity.

However, the immune response can also be triggered artificially. This involves the injection of antigens into the body. This is called artificial active immunity or vaccination.

These two main types of immunity are further categorised as passive or active immunity.

Natural acquired immunity

This may occur passively or actively.

- Natural passive immunity may be due to the transfer of antibodies from mother to foetus across the placenta or from mother to new-born offspring via colostrum, the first secretion of the mammary gland. The immunity is only temporary since no memory cells have been formed.

- Natural active immunity is achieved as a result of exposure to infection. The body manufactures its own antibodies in response to the presence of antigens on the infectious agent and also forms specific memory cells. If the same agent is encountered again it can be flooded with antibodies and eliminated before it causes disease.

Artificial acquired immunity

This also occurs passively or actively.

- Artificial passive immunity results from the injection of ready-made antibodies into the body, and again, since there are no memory cells, it is only temporary. It is useful as a preventative measure for diseases that are difficult to immunise against, such as tetanus and diphtheria. It may also be used as a treatment for certain diseases, such as rabies, where infection has already occurred and which is too dangerous to leave to the body's natural immune system. Protection is short lived because the injected antibodies are recognised as non-self and destroyed.

- Artificial active immunity (vaccination) is achieved by injecting vaccine into a healthy individual, e.g. against rubella. The body is stimulated to produce antibodies and memory cells against the antigen in the vaccine, and thus acquires immunity to subsequent infection by that disease organism.

>> *Pointer*

Vaccines are said to be 'attenuated' when the pathogen is deliberately weakened to ensure that it causes only a mild response.

 quickfire

⑥⑦ Why is passive immunity temporary?

Grade boost

Be prepared to distinguish between active and passive immunity.

>> *Pointer*

The active immunity that vaccines produce can give protection for a long time. However, several more vaccinations, called boosters, may be needed after the first vaccination.

Vaccination

Vaccination is the introduction of an antigen into the body to stimulate active immunity against a particular disease.

When the vaccine is injected into the body, lymphocytes recognise the antigens as 'non-self', and make antibodies to destroy them. This is the primary response. Memory cells then remain in the blood for a long time: these cells are capable of recognising the same antigen if it ever enters the body again, and producing the same antibodies immediately.

The graph shows the effect of immunising a child against *Rubella*, which is a virus infecting human cells. An initial injection is administered followed by a booster injection four weeks later.

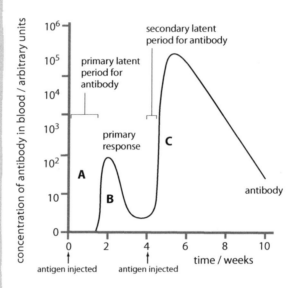

Primary and secondary responses to antibody production.

The following describes what is happening at phases A, B and C in the graph.

Phase A is called the primary latent period when the antigen is detected by B lymphocytes. These activated cells divide rapidly by mitosis forming a clone of plasma cells. Most of these cells produce antibodies but some produce memory cells.

Phase B is called the primary response period when the antibody concentration increases before decreasing again.

Phase C occurs if the antigen is reintroduced or if it persists for the duration of the primary response. This stimulates a secondary response. This is characterised by requiring a lower level of antigen with a shorter latent phase. Higher concentrations of antibody are produced for a longer period of time. This further invasion by the same pathogen triggers the same events to occur more rapidly as there is a large clone of memory cells specific to that antigen. These memory cells are activated to produce plasma B cells very quickly producing a large quantity of a specific antibody that remain for a longer period of time.

Grade boost

There are three main differences between the primary and secondary response:
- There is a delay before antibodies are produced in the primary response, but in the secondary response production is immediate.
- Larger amounts of antibodies are produced in the secondary response.
- The antibodies remain in the blood for longer during the secondary response.

68 After vaccination what happens during the latent period?

The relative effectiveness of vaccination programmes

- Vaccination has made a major contribution to reducing the incidence of certain diseases in the population. Its effectiveness increases the greater the proportion of the population is vaccinated. If there is no animal reservoir, the disease is eradicated locally and then possibly globally, as in the case of smallpox. International co-operation is essential for this to occur. The original decision to vaccinate only teenage girls against rubella was questioned. As boys could act as a reservoir of infection it was decided that they should also be vaccinated.

- Smallpox vaccination has been effective because the organism does not have a high mutation rate allowing the vaccine to remain effective. However, the influenza virus mutates frequently and causes periodic epidemics due to lack of resistance in the population and lack of effective long-term vaccination.

- There have been reports of possible side effects in a few cases of vaccination against 'childhood' diseases. This has resulted in a reduction in the 'take-up' of vaccination leading to the increase of incidence of the disease, so increasing the risk of contact. Occasionally a disease will have serious side effects in a small number of cases.

- Public information and education are therefore important to ensure rational decision making along with the identification of any contra-indications against vaccination in individual cases to minimise personal risk.

- Increased travel increases the risk of infections spreading globally. Influenza is spread by droplet infection, consequently the spread is difficult to control. The flu virus has a high mutation rate, so vaccines are not effective. Flu is a viral infection, so there is no effective curative treatment. It may have animal and bird reservoirs to act as a source of infection.

Grade boost

You should consider the relative effectiveness of specific vaccination programmes as well as the ethical considerations involved.

Grade boost

Vaccines are ineffective against pathogens that mutate frequently because the new antigens on the pathogens are no longer detected by the immune system. Mutations result in antigenic variability. An example is the influenza virus, which has many antigenic types.

 quickfire

69 Why has vaccination against smallpox been effective in eliminating the disease but this method has had only limited effect against influenza?

Grade boost

Be prepared to discuss the effectiveness of vaccination programmes.

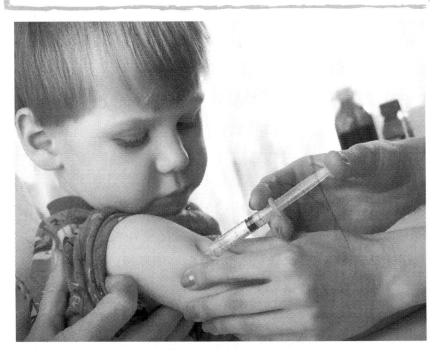

Doctor giving a child an injection.

>> Pointer

AIDS is caused by the immunodeficiency virus (HIV) which attacks helper T cells in the body's immune system. AIDS is the end stage of an HIV infection. The progress of the disease has three clinical stages. Firstly, HIV positive with no symptoms; secondly, a low T helper cell count; and finally, the symptoms of clinical AIDS.

⑩ Explain why a person who is HIV positive may not have AIDS.

⑪ Why do conditions that are normally non-fatal to the general population result in death for people with AIDS.

The effect of HIV infection

AIDS is caused by the immunodeficiency virus (HIV). HIV is a retrovirus. This means that it uses its RNA to produce a single strand of DNA, called copy DNA, inside the host's cell.

HIV is mainly transmitted in the blood or in semen. The virus enters the body through cuts in the skin or via hypodermic needles contaminated with infected blood. Individuals affected by the virus may have no symptoms other than swollen lymph glands. Others may experience a short-lived illness when they first become infected. The virus attacks helper T cells in the body's immune system.

The virus can remain latent for many years before being activated, when it will start to replicate and destroy the host cell. By reducing the number of helper T cells, HIV reduces the body's ability to fight disease. As the immune system weakens, infections that would normally be held in check start to take hold. The range of symptoms resulting from HIV infection is vast and is not the result of the HIV infection directly.

Symptoms include several forms of cancer and the sufferer may experience weight loss, fever, diarrhoea and deteriorating brain function. The most common form of death in AIDS is a rare type of pneumonia.

AIDS is actually only the end stage of an HIV infection. Shortly after the initial infection, HIV antibodies appear in the blood. The progress of infection has three clinical categories:

1. HIV positive with little or no symptoms.
2. Some symptoms, low helper T cell count.
3. Clinical AIDS, symptoms appear.

Graph showing rise in AIDS and HIV.

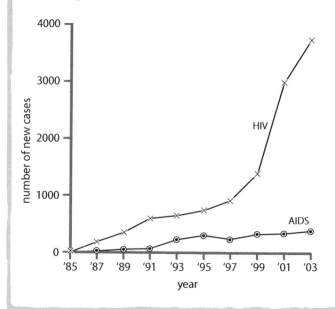

Pathogens, the spread of human disease and the control of infection

Key Terms

Pathogen = any micro-organism that causes a disease by infecting a host.

Vectors = organisms that carry pathogens from one organism to another.

The human body acts as a host to a number of other living organisms. Some are useful, such as the natural bacterial flora on the skin, some cause irritation but superficial damage, for example the fungus which causes athlete's foot. However, a number of organisms are harmful and cause disease. All the main groups of micro-organisms – viruses, bacteria, fungi and protoctista include species that may cause disease in humans. Several classes of worms also cause disease. Selected examples of these diseases will be studied in this section.

Disease transmission

Many diseases in humans are caused by **pathogenic** bacteria or viruses. These micro-organisms may be transmitted from one person to another in a variety of ways:

- Airborne transmission, also called droplet infection, is the main method by which diseases of the lungs and respiratory passages are spread. The micro-organisms are expelled in tiny droplets of saliva and mucus as a result of sneezing, coughing, or even just breathing. Bacterial diseases spread this way include whooping cough and tuberculosis, while viral infections include influenza and measles.

- Transmission via food and water – these can become contaminated with bacteria if sanitation and hygiene are poor. Salmonella food poisoning is spread in or from the undercooked meat of infected animals while diseases such as cholera and typhoid are mainly spread through the contamination of water by the untreated faeces of infected individuals.

- Direct contact or with the aid of **vectors**. An example is the mosquito, which acts as a vector for the protoctistan *Plasmodium* which causes malaria.

A disease which is always present at low levels in an area is described as endemic. An epidemic occurs when there is a significant increase in the usual number of cases of a disease often associated with a rapid spread.

A disease that can be passed from host to host is termed an infectious disease, whereas diseases spread by direct contact are described as contagious. A carrier is a person who shows no symptoms when infected by a disease organism but can pass the disease on to another individual.

The place where a pathogen is normally found is its reservoir. This may be in humans or another animal and may be a source of infection.

quickfire

㉒ What is the difference between an endemic disease and an epidemic of a disease?

» Pointer

It is essential to learn the various definitions relating to disease transmission.

The control and treatment of selected diseases

>> *Pointer*

For each disease, you should be able to describe: the name of the organism that causes the disease; the tissue affected; the symptoms; the source of infection; the mode of transmission; the prevention; control methods and treatment.

quickfire

⑦③ Why is it important to allow a frozen chicken to thaw completely before cooking?

quickfire

⑦④ Explain why there is a time interval of several hours between ingesting *Salmonella* and the appearance of symptoms. Explain the cause of the symptoms.

>> *Pointer*

TB is showing a worldwide increase partly due to the link with the AIDS epidemic and also due to some strains of the bacterium becoming resistant to antibiotics.

>> *Pointer*

Tuberculin is a harmless extract made from *Mycobacterium tuberculosis* which contains antigens like those from the live bacterium.

Diseases caused by bacteria

Salmonella food poisoning is caused by a Gram-negative, rod-shaped bacterium. **Toxins**, produced by the bacterium, affect the gut lining causing diarrhoea and vomiting. It is commonly found in animal intestines and may be transferred to meat at animal slaughter. The bacterium multiplies during storage of infected food. Good hygiene practices are essential to avoid food poisoning. These include thorough cooking, storage in cool conditions, separation of cooked and uncooked meat and the prevention of contamination from carriers. Analysis of antigenic types may enable the tracing of the source of an infection.

Antibiotic treatment is possible but is used only when essential to prevent the build-up of resistance. A vaccine is not available as there are over 2000 antigenic types.

Cholera is an acute intestinal infection caused by a Gram-negative bacterium endemic in some areas of the world. The bacterium produces toxins that affect the gut lining causing watery diarrhoea and leading to severe dehydration and possibly death. Humans can act as a reservoir and as carriers. Cholera is spread by contaminated water and food. Sudden large outbreaks are usually caused by a contaminated water supply.

Protective measures include hygienic disposal of human faeces, providing a supply of safe drinking water, hygienic preparation of food (preventing contamination of food, and cooking food thoroughly).

Powerful antibiotic therapy is possible but treatment is largely by re-hydration. Vaccine may provide temporary protection.

Tuberculosis (TB) is a bacterial disease that was thought to be almost completely eradicated but in recent years it is again on the increase. It is estimated that eight million cases are added annually and that TB causes two million human deaths each year worldwide. The most common form of TB attacks the lungs and lymph nodes in the neck. The bacteria may remain in the lungs or lymph system for years before becoming active. The symptoms are a persistent cough, chest pain, coughing up blood, fever, night sweats and weight loss due to a lack of appetite. The bacterium is transmitted in airborne droplets when infected people cough and sneeze. It can spread rapidly in overcrowded conditions.

In the UK in the late 1940s there was a large decrease in the incidence of TB through the introduction of antibiotics, together with improved housing conditions.

Prevention involves a school vaccination programme whereby In the UK, BCG vaccine is given to pupils between the ages of 10–14. Before the vaccine is administered, each pupil is given the Heaf test which involves injecting tuberculin into the skin to check whether the individual is already immune to

TB. If the test is positive the individual's lymphocytes have responded to the test injection and caused an inflammation as the lymphocytes act against the antigen. If, however, there is little or no response to the test, then the BCG vaccination will be given. Unfortunately no vaccine is available to provide reliable protection for adults.

Diseases caused by viruses

Several highly significant human diseases are caused by viruses, including rubella, shingles, measles, poliomyelitis, influenza and HIV.

Influenza is caused by a virus consisting of a central strand of RNA, coated in protein, surrounded by an outer lipoprotein coat.

- It infects cells of the lining of the upper respiratory tract, especially the nose and throat. Deaths can occur due to secondary respiratory infections by bacteria causing bronchitis and pneumonia.
- Transmission is by droplet infection, coughing and sneezing. Transmission is more likely in crowded and poorly ventilated places.
- The incubation period (the time between infection and the development of symptoms) is about two days. The symptoms may last up to four days and include headache, sore throat, fever, a rise in body temperature, with shivering.
- Prevention includes quarantine and hygiene but it is a difficult mode of spread to control.
- Antibiotic treatment has no effect therefore symptoms are treated as necessary. That is, rest, aspirin, and plenty of fluids to relieve the symptoms.
- Vaccines are available but due to the number of antigenic types and the regular emergence of new ones, they are not always effective.
- However, in the UK a vaccination programme is available to protect particularly susceptible individuals, especially the very young and elderly.

Malaria

Malaria is not caused by a bacterium or virus but by a single-celled organism belonging to the protoctist group. *Plasmodium* is a **parasite** which infects liver and red blood cells. it is carried from one person to another by the female mosquito. The mosquito is called a vector because it transmits the disease.

The life cycle of *Plasmodium* takes place in the human body and the female mosquito acts as a secondary host. It is endemic in some sub-tropical regions.

The infection is acquired by a human when an adult female mosquito, already infected with the malarial parasite, inserts its mouthparts into the individual's skin, discharges saliva, which contains an anti-coagulant, and sucks up blood. Thousands of the microscopic *Plasmodium* are injected with the saliva into the blood of the human. Within a few hours the parasites have entered the liver cells of the host. Here they feed, grow and multiply asexually to produce large

Key Term

Parasite = an organism that lives in or on another living organism, called the host, derives food from the host and causes it harm.

» Pointer

Patients with TB are treated with antibiotics. Rather than the usual short course of treatment the antibiotic must be taken for a long period (6–12 months) to entirely eliminate the bacterium from the body.

quickfire

⑦⑤ What is meant by the term 'incubation period'?

quickfire

⑦⑥ Suggest why annual vaccinations for flu may be ineffective.

numbers. The parasites also enter red blood cells where they again multiply asexually. The liver cells eventually burst to release large numbers of *Plasmodium* to infect more red blood cells.

>> **Pointer**

You are not required to learn details such as the names of the stages of the life cycle.

>> **Pointer**

Malaria is a serious pandemic disease affecting up to 300 million people in the tropics each year!

⑦ Explain why one of the symptoms of malaria is fever.

>> **Pointer**

Interrupting the cycle of transmission from mosquito to human is the main aim in controlling the spread of malaria.

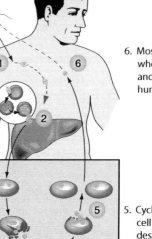

1. Bite from an infected mosquito

2. Parasite starts reproducing in the liver, some parasites remaining dormant for years before becoming activated

3. In the blood stream, further reproduction occurs within red blood cells

4. Parasite reproduction results in further red blood cell infection

5. Cycles of red blood cell infection and destruction coincide with fever and chills

6. Mosquito takes up parasite when feeding on blood and transmits it to a new human host

Life cycle of malarial parasite.

As the cycle of infection is repeated, toxins from the cells of the parasite accumulate in the bloodstream, causing severe bouts of fever. Symptoms appear one to two weeks after being bitten. Symptoms include headaches, chills and fever. Malaria caused by *P. falciparum* is the most severe, with high fever, coma and convulsions and can be fatal within a few days of the first symptoms.

Eventually some of the parasites develop into sexual stages which remain dormant in the bloodstream. When this infected human blood is taken in by a feeding mosquito the life cycle is completed. The parasite migrates to the salivary glands of the mosquito and may be injected into a new host.

Most efforts to control malaria are aimed at destroying the mosquito and so interrupting the cycle of transmission. There are three main ways of achieving this:

1. Preventing the mosquito from biting humans by:
   - Hanging nets treated with insecticide around beds to protect them against being bitten while asleep.
   - Wearing protective clothing.
   - Using insect repellents.
2. Eliminating the vector (the mosquito) by:
   - Draining swamps where the mosquito lays its eggs and where the larvae develop. This is very expensive and it is impossible to drain all breeding areas.
   - Spraying the breeding grounds with diesel oil – the oil is taken into the breathing tubes of the larvae and kills them.
   - Spraying insecticides on the surfaces of ponds and lakes to kill the larvae.
   - Using biological control methods – using fish (guppies) to eat larvae, bacteria to infect larvae, sterilisation of males to reduce breeding.
3. Attacking the parasite: This is difficult as the parasite spends most of its life inside body cells. Therefore control methods are directed against *Plasmodium* while in the human bloodstream. These have limited effectiveness and have side effects.
   - Quinine is the oldest drug used but has now been replaced by synthetic anti-malarial drugs which are more effective – this method merely reduces the chances of infection.
   - Vaccines have proved difficult to develop because the malarial parasite mutates and there are different antigenic types.

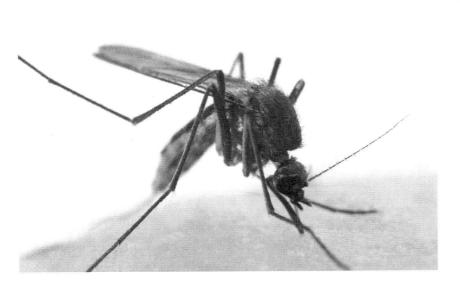

Grade boost

Compile a list of the advantages and disadvantages of the methods of controlling malaria.

 quickfire

⑦⑧ Explain how spraying oil on the surface of water prevents the transmission of malaria.

Grade boost

Be prepared to write an essay 'Describe the methods that can be used to control the spread of malaria'.

⟫ Pointer

You may have wondered why the life cycle of *Plasmodium* is so complicated and why it has a primary and a secondary host. Blood parasites are not 'safe' within the primary host, the human. Whilst in the bloodstream they are the target of specific immune attack so they take refuge by invading host cells. They need a secondary host, the mosquito, to spread to other primary hosts.

Key Terms

Bactericidal = bacteria are killed directly.

Bacteriostatic = inhibits the growth of bacteria.

Agar = nutrient medium used to grow bacteria.

>> *Pointer*

Disinfectants are different from other antimicrobial agents such as antibiotics, which destroy micro-organisms within the body, and antiseptics, which destroy micro-organisms on living tissue.

⑦⑨ In the diagram opposite which is the most effective antibiotic in destroying the bacteria growing on the agar?

Antibiotics

Antibiotics are chemicals produced by micro-organisms, bacteria and fungi, which at low concentration inhibit the growth of pathogens. They may be **bactericidal** or **bacteriostatic**. To be effective all antibiotics must have selective toxicity, that is, they should kill or inhibit the growth of micro-organisms without damaging the host.

Consider a patient visiting the doctor with a throat or chest infection. The doctor may prescribe a broad spectrum antibiotic. This has the disadvantage that the antibiotic targets not only the pathogen but also much of the body's normal flora. The normal microbial community controls the growth of pathogens by competing with them. By removing these 'useful' microbes, certain microbes that do not normally cause problems may flourish and become opportunistic pathogens.

If the infection persists after the initial treatment with the broad spectrum antibiotic, the doctor may send a throat swab to the hospital pathology laboratory for screening. This involves growing the microbe on **agar** plates. Different antibiotics absorbed onto filter paper discs are then placed on the surface of the agar and the plate is incubated at 37°C for 24 hours. The antibiotic diffuses out of each filter paper disc, killing the microbe and producing a clear area, called a zone of inhibition. The greater the diameter of the clear area, the more effective is the antibiotic against the microbe. The results are sent to the doctor who then prescribes the most effective antibiotic.

Agar plate showing typical results using a sensitivity test .

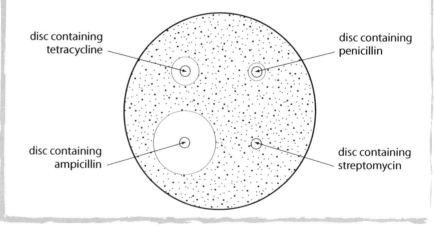

disc containing tetracycline

disc containing penicillin

disc containing ampicillin

disc containing streptomycin

How antibiotics work

⑧⓪ Give an example of a broad spectrum antibiotic.

Antibiotics can be divided into two groups:

- 'Broad spectrum' antibiotics such as chloramphenicol and tetracycline are effective against a wide range of pathogenic bacteria. These antibiotics affect widespread microbial processes such as protein synthesis.

- 'Narrow spectrum' antibiotics such as penicillin are effective against a limited range of pathogens. These antibiotics affect more specific processes such as cell wall formation.

The Gram stain technique distinguishes two groups of bacteria, those that are Gram-positive and those that are Gram-negative. The different staining properties of these two groups of bacteria are due to differences in the chemical composition of their cell walls. An understanding of cell wall structure also enables us to understand how narrow spectrum antibiotics, such as penicillin, kill bacteria.

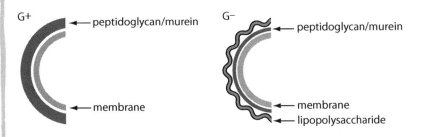

Bacterial cell wall structure.

Gram-positive bacteria lack lipopolysaccharide in their walls and do retain crystal violet. These are more susceptible to antibiotics and to the enzyme, lysozyme, which occurs in human tears, than Gram-negative bacteria. The Gram-positive bacteria include *Staphylococcus* and *Streptococcus*. This group appears a violet colour when viewed under the microscope.

Water passes into bacterial cells by osmosis but the peptidoglycan cell wall prevents osmotic lysis. Penicillin kills bacteria by inhibiting the enzyme necessary for the cross linking of the cell wall. As the bacterium grows the cell wall becomes progressively weaker and the cell takes up water and swells. The cell wall is unable to withstand the pressure and the cell bursts.

Gram-negative bacteria, e.g. *Salmonella* sp, have chemically complex walls where a thinner layer of peptidoglycan (murein) is surrounded by an outer layer of lipoprotein and lipopolysaccharide. They do not retain dyes like crystal violet. They appear red when viewed under the microscope. The bacteria are resistant to the antibiotic penicillin. These bacteria are acted upon by antibiotics which inhibit protein synthesis. For example, streptomycin inhibits growth by locking on to the ribosomes of the bacteria preventing protein synthesis taking place.

Antibiotic resistance

Many bacteria that were previously susceptible to antibiotics have now become resistant. Resistance to a chemical poison is the ability of an organism to survive exposure to a dose of that poison which would normally be lethal to it. This resistance has arisen because of random mutations. Mutations are rare but as bacteria multiply rapidly, one every 20 minutes under optimum conditions, a greater rate of mutation occurs. Most gene mutations are recessive and rarely expressed in combination with a dominant gene. However, repeated exposure to antibiotics has led to more bacteria surviving and passing on resistant genes.

Grade boost
The cross linking provides strength and the cell wall protects against osmotic lysis.

≫ Pointer
An understanding of cell wall structure helps to understand how antibiotics work.

Grade boost
Human cells don't have cell walls, so penicillin does not affect the growth of our cells.

≫ Pointer
Do not be concerned with the details of protein synthesis. This topic is studied at A2 level.

Grade boost
Because bacterial ribosomes are different from those of the human, streptomycin does not interfere with protein synthesis in the patient taking the drug.

⊙≪≪≪ quickfire

81 Explain how the prevention of cell wall formation kills bacteria.

quickfire

82 What is meant by the term 'resistance'?

>> **Pointer**
The resistance of bacteria to antibiotics has increased due to their overuse in treating humans and also use in animal feed.

quickfire

83 Name a bacterium that is resistant to several antibiotics.

- The use of antibiotics to treat disease in the human population has had obvious benefits. However, in agriculture, many farm animals are reared indoors so that they grow more rapidly, e.g. birds kept in confined areas. In these crowded conditions there is a greater risk of disease spreading; therefore broad spectrum antibiotics are often added to animal food in an attempt to prevent disease. Although the prophylactic (applying antibiotics to prevent infection) use of small quantities of antibiotics in animal feed has led to healthier, faster-growing animals, this widespread increased use of antibiotics has led to the development of resistance among many species of bacteria.

- In the past antibiotics have perhaps been prescribed too readily by many doctors in general practice (GPs). Reducing the number of antibiotics in use means that fewer bacteria are exposed to them and reduces the chances of resistant strains appearing.

- Resistance arises by mutations occurring randomly within populations of organisms which then confer an advantage in the presence of that antibiotic. This may be the ability to produce an enzyme which breaks down the antibiotic. For example, some bacteria have developed an enzyme, penicillinase, which renders penicillin ineffective. In the presence of penicillin, non-resistant forms are destroyed. There is a selection pressure favouring the resistant types. The greater the quantity and frequency of penicillin use, the greater the selection pressure.

- The problem has been made worse by the discovery that resistance can be transmitted between indiuals of the same species. There is evidence that resistance may be passed from one organism to another on **plasmids** during conjugation (sexual reproduction). This means that a disease-causing organism can become resistant to a given antibiotic even before the antibiotic is used against it.

- MRSA (methicillin resistant *Staphylococcus aureus*) has developed a resistance to several antibiotics. Antibiotics are widely used in hospitals, especially to prevent infections occurring from surgery. This organism originated in Australia and within ten years has spread worldwide. A sample of *Pseudomonas aeruginosa* has been identified as being resistant to all clinical antibiotics.

- Such organisms are becoming a more common problem and the antibiotics available to treat them are becoming very limited in number.

Antibiotics and viruses

>> **Pointer**
Viruses do not have metabolic pathways and are unaffected by antibiotics.

Viruses are not affected by antibiotics. A GP examining a patient with a suspected infection may diagnose a viral cause and therefore not prescribe any medication but advise the patient to keep warm and drink plenty of fluids. Viruses are extremely small and are made up of DNA or RNA surrounded by a protein coat. Viruses do not have a cell wall and do not have metabolic pathways. The treatment of viral infections is also difficult because viruses are intracellular parasites that are only capable of reproducing inside living host cells. Drugs may not penetrate these cells, and if they did they may damage them.

Parasitism

All animals struggle to survive, to avoid competition with others, and to avoid being preyed upon by other animals. Parasites have become specialised and undergone considerable evolutionary changes in order to survive in the host.

Parasitism is a specialised form of heterotrophic nutrition. A parasite is an organism that lives on or in another organism, called the host, and obtains nourishment at the expense of the host. Some parasites cause little harm but most are potentially more serious and may lead to death. Many organisms are parasitised for at least part of their lives. Plants are parasitised by bacteria, fungi, viruses, nematodes and insects; animals are parasitised by bacteria, fungi, viruses, protoctista, tapeworms, nematodes, insects and mites. Even bacteria are parasitised by viruses called bacteriophages!

Multicellular parasites are made up of more than a single cell and are relatively complex organisms. Some **endoparasites**, such as tapeworms, flukes and roundworms, cause harm directly and are highly specialised to live inside their hosts. Some insects and arachnids are **ectoparasites**.

The following section deals with selected parasites including the head louse, the tapeworm, roundworm and fluke. Each species has adapted to its specialised way of life. Because they often live within the host they have the advantage of not having to search for food. In fact, they are often surrounded by food! Consequently, they often lack some of the features of their free-living relatives. They may have no digestive system or sensory organs and have limited powers of movement and co-ordination.

In studying the parasite species that follow, consider how each has become specialised by having:

- A means of entry into the host tissue.
- Devices to keep the parasite attached to the host.
- Mechanisms to resist counter-attacks by the host's immune system.
- A degeneration of unnecessary organ systems, leading to a simplified digestive tract, means of movement, or nervous system.
- Mechanisms to overcome the problem of transfer to an intermediate host and the production of vast numbers of eggs or offspring.
- A means of transmission between hosts which may require a resistant stage; intermediate host.
- A high rate of reproduction to produce large numbers of offspring.

Pediculus – the head louse

The head louse is an ectoparasite feeding on blood but can live for short periods away from the body. It affects only humans and cannot be passed on to, or caught from, animals. It is a tiny, wingless insect which feeds by sucking blood from the scalp. It has a short life cycle and reproduces rapidly with numbers increasing alarmingly if not treated. The eggs are called nits and

Pointer

You have already studied the malarial parasite, *Plasmodium*, on page 101.

Pointer

The study of parasites is of economic importance as they cause disease in humans, domesticated animals and crops.

Grade boost

Detailed lifecycles of these organisms are not needed. You are instead required to know how the parasites have become adapted to their specialised way of life, often, in the case of endoparasites, living in the hostile environment within the host.

Grade boost

More highly evolved parasites have more than one host species. It is important for their survival to have a secondary or intermediate host because if the host dies then so does the parasite. However, transferring to another host is a hazardous process as the parasite is exposed to conditions outside the body of the host. Consequently, parasites have a high rate of reproduction to produce large numbers of offspring.

84 Name the secondary host of *Schistosoma*.

85 Describe how *Schistosoma* is transmitted from its secondary host to a human.

Grade boost

Be prepared to explain how the means of entry into their host differs in the various parasites and where in the human body the parasite is mainly found.

are laid glued to the base of hairs. The insect has adapted to grasping and attaching to the fine hairs of the head by having claws on the end of its legs. It is able to walk from one hair to another and is transferred by close hair-to-hair contact.

The symptom is itching of the scalp. Insecticides for treating head lice are available as lotions, liquids or cream rinses and are very effective.

Schistosoma – the blood fluke

Schistosomes are specialised parasitic flatworms. They are specialised for living in the blood vessels supplying the intestine or the bladder. Schistosomes cause the disease schistosomiasis or bilharzia, one of the most widespread and devastating parasitic diseases in humans. It is endemic in 74 developing countries, particularly in Africa and eastern Asia, where fishing and washing in streams carries a high risk of infection.

In intestinal schistosomiasis there is progressive enlargement of the spleen and liver and intestinal damage and bleeding. The disease has a low mortality rate but sufferers become severely weakened. One symptom of the disease is anaemia. Transmission of the parasite occurs in freshwater when intermediate snail hosts release infective larval forms of the parasite. The larvae penetrate the skin of areas exposed when humans wash or go fishing.

The larvae enter a vein and then pass through the body in the blood stream, moving through the lungs and liver, where they mature. They then leave the liver and move to the blood vessels surrounding the intestine or bladder. They feed on red blood cells and the female produces a large number of eggs. Some eggs escape into the gut cavity and are shed into the faeces or urine. These eggs hatch into a new form of larva which infects an intermediate host, the snail. These multiply further in the snail and are released into the water to infect a human host.

Prescribed drugs are an effective treatment.

Ascaris – the roundworm

Ascaris is the most common human worm infection with infection occurring worldwide. It is most common in tropical and sub-tropical areas where sanitation and hygiene are poor. It is estimated that 1.2 billion people are infected! Children are affected more often than adults.

Ascaris lives in the small intestine. A female worm can grow up to 40 cm long and weigh 9 grams. Many worms can live in the intestine during infection. If the infection is light no symptoms are noticeable but in children the infection may cause slow growth and slower weight gain. Heavy infection can cause abdominal pain. Extremely heavy infection may cause a blockage of the intestine.

The female worm can produce 200,000 eggs a day in the intestine. The eggs are passed out of the body and are found in human faeces. Children can become infected after touching the mouth with hands that have been contaminated with eggs from the soil or other contaminating surfaces, or by ingesting contaminated food or water. The eggs hatch in the intestine and can penetrate the lining, pass into the blood vessels and travel to the lungs. There the larvae break out of the alveoli and are coughed up and swallowed.

Prescribed drugs are an effective treatment.

Taenia solium – the pork tapeworm

Imagine living in the gut of another animal! The tapeworm is ribbon-like and can be up to 10 metres long! It has a 'head' made up of muscle on which are suckers and hooks and its body consists of a linear series of thin 'segments'. The pork tapeworm has two hosts. The primary host is the human and the pig is the secondary host. The pig becomes infected if it feeds in drainage channels contaminated by human faeces. Humans are infected by eating undercooked infected pork.

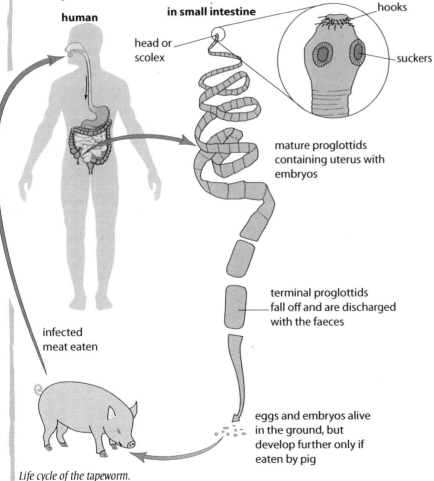

Life cycle of the tapeworm.

>> *Pointer*

The human gut parasite (*Taenia solium*) is a particularly good example of a highly evolved parasite.

Grade boost

The tapeworm does not have a gut. This is because it is surrounded by the host's digested materials, which are absorbed through the body surface of the parasite.

86 Name the secondary host of *Taenia solium*.

Grade boost

The tapeworm is hermaphrodite, that is, both sex organs are present in the one individual. The gut could not accommodate two tapeworms so mating would be impossible. It therefore fertilises its own eggs.

87 State two of the problems that the tapeworm has to overcome living in the hostile environment of the gut of the host.

88 State two adaptations exhibited by the tapeworm to its parasitic way of life.

》Pointer

The adult worms cause little discomfort but, if the eggs are eaten by humans, dormant embryos form cysts in various organs and can damage the surrounding tissue. Adults can be treated with appropriate drugs. Public health measures and frequent inspection of meat are essential.

89 What is the advantage to *Taenia* of a high rate of reproduction?

》Pointer

Consider how the tapeworm lifecycle conforms to the requirements listed on page 107.

Although the tapeworm lives in an immediate source of food, it needs to survive the hostile conditions found in the gut.

The following are the problems that the gut parasite has to overcome in order to survive:

- It lives surrounded by digestive juices and mucus. It has to survive the extreme conditions of pH along the length of the gut.
- Food, mixed with digestive juices, is in constant motion as it is churned about as well as being propelled along the length of the gut by peristaltic contractions of the muscular wall.
- The immune system of the host.
- Death of the host results in the death of the parasite.

The tapeworm has evolved the following structural modifications to enable it to live as a parasite:

- Suckers and a double row of curved hooks for attachment to the wall of the gut.
- A body covering which protects it from the host's immune responses.
- A thick cuticle and the production of inhibitory substances on the surface of the segments to prevent their digestion by the host's enzymes.
- Because it lives in a stable environment it does not need to move around and does not require a sensory system. This has led to the degeneration of unnecessary organs. It does have simple excretory and nervous systems but most of the body is concerned with reproduction.
- The tapeworm is very thin and has a large surface area to volume ratio. It is surrounded by digested food so it has a very simple digestive system and pre-digested food can be absorbed over the entire body surface.
- Because the gut could not accommodate two tapeworms, each segment contains both male and female reproductive organs. Vast numbers of eggs are produced, with each mature segment containing up to 40,000 eggs. The mature segments pass out of the host's body with the faeces.

The eggs have resistant shells and can survive until eaten by the secondary host. Further development can then take place and the embryos which hatch from the eggs move into the muscles of the pig and remain dormant until the meat of the pig is eaten by a human.

Summary of the adaptations of selected parasites studied.

Name of parasite	Head louse	Tapeworm
Entry to host	Ectoparasite	Eating infected uncooked meat
Attachment devices	Claws for grasping hair	Suckers and hooks
Resistance to host's immune system	None	Thick cuticle and inhibitory secretions
Organ degeneration	Wingless insect	No organs of movement or sense organs
Transfer to intermediate host	No intermediate host	Eggs have resistant coats/ larvae dormant in pig
Reproduction	Large number of eggs	Enormous number of eggs

Grade boost

Create a similar table that includes bloodfluke and roundworm.

Summary: Biodiversity and Physiology of Body System

Biodiversity and evolution

- Evolution
- Adaptive radiation
- Classification
- Five kingdom classification
- Human evolution

Uptake of energy and nutrients

- Food is processed by ingestion, digestion, absorption and egestion
- As humans have a varied diet, the gut is divided into specialised regions for digestion and absorption
- Chemical digestion involves enzymes which hydrolyse large insoluble materials
- The end products of digestion are glucose, amino acids, fatty acids and glycerol
- Digested products are absorbed in the ileum by diffusion, facilitated diffusion or by active transport
- Conditions affecting the digestive system include cancer, coeliac disease, diverticulitis and ulceration

Transport to and from exchange surfaces

- Blood is made up of plasma, red blood cells and white blood cells
  - Red blood cells contain haemoglobin
  - White blood cells involved in defence against disease
  - Fluid from the plasma escapes through the walls of capillaries to form tissue fluid
- Abnormal destruction or loss of blood cells gives rise to anaemia
- Individuals belong to one of four blood groups, A, B, AB and O
- Transport of materials in humans involves:
  - Vessels – arteries, veins and capillaries
  - A muscular pump – the heart
  - Three main phases of heart beat – atrial systole, ventricular systole and diastole
  - Heart muscle is myogenic and controlled by specialised regions of cardiac fibres

- Blood pressure may be monitored using a sphygmomanometer
- A number of factors can cause increased blood pressure or hypertension
- Heart function may be analysed using an electrocardiogram
- Heart surgery may involve angioplasty or a coronary bypass
- Carbon dioxide is mainly carried in the form of hydrogen carbonate ions and the chloride shift maintains the electrochemical neutrality of the red blood cell
- The oxygen dissociation curve shows the response of haemoglobin when it is exposed to a gradual increase in oxygen tension

Gas exchange

- Humans have lungs as a specialised exchange surface
- They ventilate the lungs by negative pressure breathing
- A spirometer is used to measure the pattern of change in lung volume during breathing
- Conditions affecting breathing include asthma and emphysema
- Smoking has short- and long-term effects on the lungs

Human defence mechanisms

- Defence against disease involves physical barriers such as the skin
- Damage to the skin triggers localised defence mechanisms such as inflammation and phagocytosis
- Immunity is a specific systemic response acquired during a lifetime
- Immune responses may be humoral or cell-mediated
- Antibodies bind with specific antigens and destroy them
- AIDS is caused by a virus which attacks cells in the body's immune system
- Immunity may be naturally acquired or may be artificially acquired when it follows vaccination
- Vaccination programmes have been successful against some viruses but not all

Pathogens, the spread of human disease and the control of infection

- Diseases are transmitted from one person to another in a variety of ways
- Diseases caused by bacteria include salmonella food poisoning, cholera and tuberculosis
- Diseases caused by viruses include influenza and HIV
- The vector of the malarial parasite, *Plasmodium*, is the mosquito
- Since *Plasmodium* spends most of its life inside body cells, efforts to control malaria are mainly aimed at killing the mosquito
- Antibiotics such as penicillin are effective in destroying bacteria by affecting cell wall formation
- Broad spectrum antibiotics destroy bacteria by preventing protein synthesis
- Many bacteria previously susceptible to antibiotics have now become resistant
- Parasitism is a specialised form of heterotrophic nutrition
- Human parasites include the head louse, blood fluke, roundworm and tapeworm
- Endoparasites are highly specialised to living inside their hosts.

Biodiversity and evolution

1(a) Table 1 provides some features of three kingdoms of living organisms.
Complete the table by stating the name of each kingdom. (3)

Table 1

Features	Kingdom
Unicellular, no nuclear membrane, cell walls made of murein and not cellulose.	
Thread-like hyphae forming a mycelium, cell wall made of chitin.	
Multicellular, cells have cellulose cell wall.	

(b) Table 2 gives some details of human classification, in hierarchical order.

Table 2

Taxon	Human
Kingdom	Animalia
	Chordata
	Mammalia
	Primates
	Hominidae
	Homo
Species	*sapiens*

Name the class and the family to which the human belongs. (2)

(c) (i) Fossil evidence suggests that *Homo sapiens* and *Homo neanderthalensis* coexisted for at least 40,000 years. State why these two human forms might be classified as separate species despite having many common features. (2)

(ii) Name a biological technique that can be used to confirm that *H.sapiens* and *H.neanderthalensis* are separate species. (1)

WJEC HB2 MAY 2011

2 The following list of terms concerns organisms and their evolution.

A	biodiversity	D	variation	G	isolation
B	evolution	E	taxonomy	H	speciation
C	palaeontology	F	extinction	I	competition

Below are five statements. Select from the above list the letter for the appropriate term that matches the statement. (5)

(a) The study of plants and animals of the geological past as represented by their fossil remains.

(b) The loss of species.

(c) The process by which new species are formed from pre-existing ones over long periods of time.

(d) A measure of the number of species on the planet.

(e) The appearance of a new species.

WJEC HB2 JAN 2010

Uptake of energy and nutrients

1 (a) Describe how and where the human gut digests and absorbs proteins. (6)

(b) Discuss the causes, symptoms and treatment of coeliac disease. (4)

WJEC HB2 JAN 2010

2 (a) Complete the following table to indicate where in the gut chemical digestion of each class of food begins. (3)

Food class	Where digestion begins
Carbohydrate	
Protein	
Fat	

(b) Explain the difference in action of exopeptidase and endopeptidase. (2)

WJEC BI4 JAN 2004

3 The diagram represents the human digestive system.

(a) Using the appropriate letters shown on the diagram, identify the following. (4)

(i) An acidic region.

(ii) The region where the hydrolysis of protein begins.

(iii) Two regions where the enzyme amylase is produced.

(iv) The structure which produces chemicals which emulsify fats.

(b) In the villi of the small intestine what is the function of:

(i) The lacteal? (1)

(ii) The capillaries? (1)

(iii) The smooth muscle cells? (1)

(c) Patients with colon cancer may have their colon surgically removed.
Explain why they are likely to suffer from symptoms of dehydration. (1)

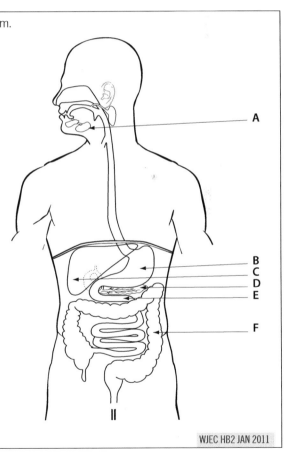

WJEC HB2 JAN 2011

Gas exchange

1   The diagram shows a human alveolus.

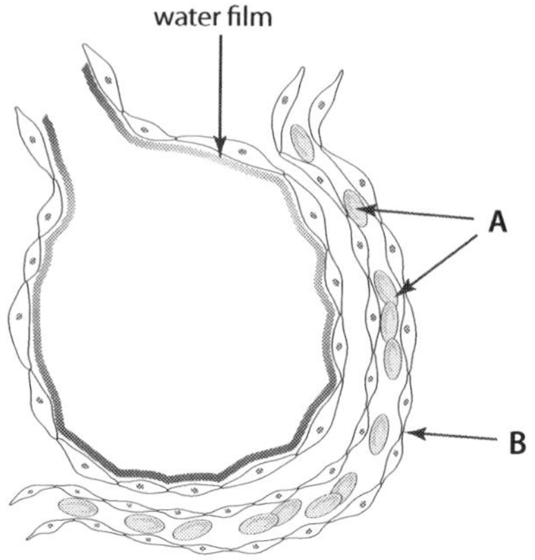

(a) (i) Name cells A and B. (2)

   (ii) What is the function of the surfactant found on the inner surface of the alveolus? (1)

   (iii) Suggest one medical use for a similar artificial surfactant. (1)

(b)   The graphs show two spirometer traces while a student was running on a treadmill. In C the treadmill is set so that she is running on the level whereas in D it is set so that she is running at the same pace up a gradient.

water film

A

B

C

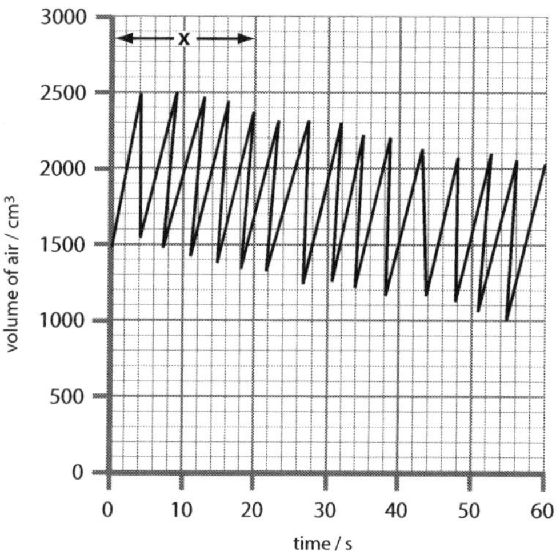

D

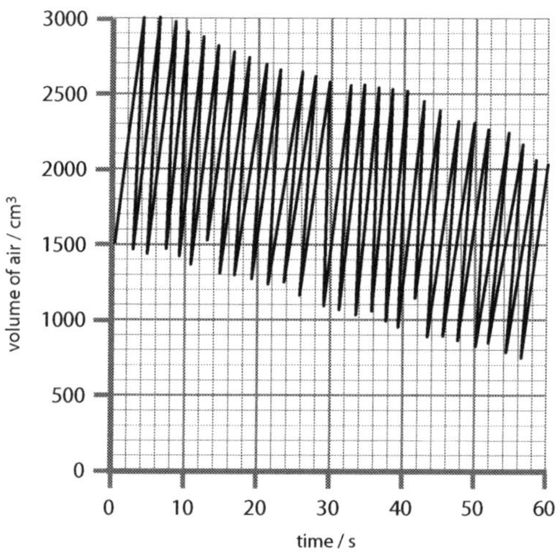

(i) State two differences in breathing shown on traces C and D. (2)

(ii) State the number of complete breaths per minute recorded on trace C. (1)

(iii) What is the difference between the students' tidal volumes shown by traces C and D? (1)

(iv) How would you expect the tidal volume in region X of trace C to differ if the student suffered from asthma? (1)

WJEC HB2 JAN 2010

---

2 (a)   Describe the mechanism of inspiration of the lungs. (4)

 (b)   Describe the effects of smoking on the respiratory system. (6)

WJEC HB2 JAN 2009

Transport to and from exchange surfaces

1   The diagram shows part of the human circulatory system.

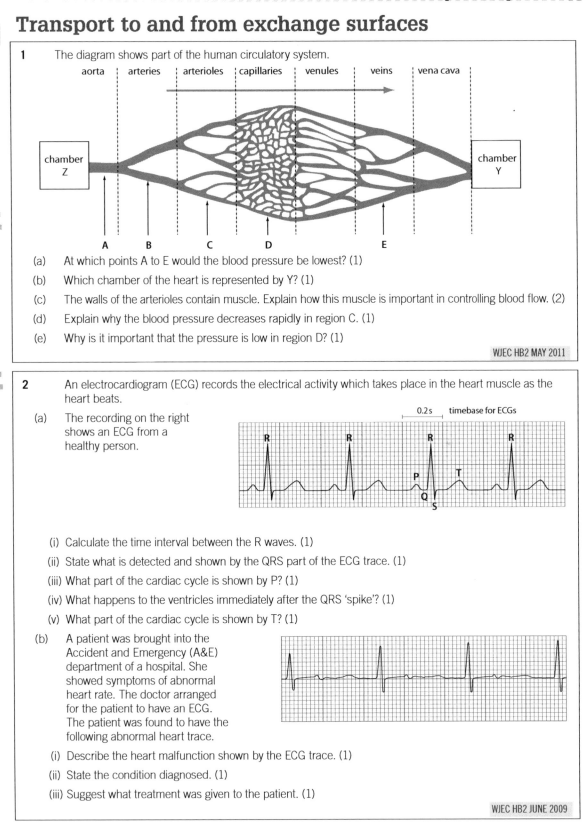

(a)   At which points A to E would the blood pressure be lowest? (1)

(b)   Which chamber of the heart is represented by Y? (1)

(c)   The walls of the arterioles contain muscle. Explain how this muscle is important in controlling blood flow. (2)

(d)   Explain why the blood pressure decreases rapidly in region C. (1)

(e)   Why is it important that the pressure is low in region D? (1)

WJEC HB2 MAY 2011

2   An electrocardiogram (ECG) records the electrical activity which takes place in the heart muscle as the heart beats.

(a)   The recording on the right shows an ECG from a healthy person.

(i)   Calculate the time interval between the R waves. (1)

(ii) State what is detected and shown by the QRS part of the ECG trace. (1)

(iii) What part of the cardiac cycle is shown by P? (1)

(iv) What happens to the ventricles immediately after the QRS 'spike'? (1)

(v)   What part of the cardiac cycle is shown by T? (1)

(b)   A patient was brought into the Accident and Emergency (A&E) department of a hospital. She showed symptoms of abnormal heart rate. The doctor arranged for the patient to have an ECG. The patient was found to have the following abnormal heart trace.

(i)   Describe the heart malfunction shown by the ECG trace. (1)

(ii) State the condition diagnosed. (1)

(iii) Suggest what treatment was given to the patient. (1)

WJEC HB2 JUNE 2009

Human defence mechanisms

1   There are two main types of immune response. These are labelled type 1 and type 2 in the diagram.

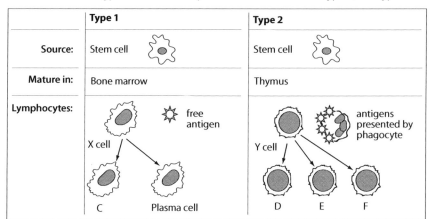

(a)   Name response types 1 and 2. (2)

(b)   Name the cells X and Y. (2)

(c)   Where in the body are the stem cells shown in the diagram produced? (1)

(d)   Plasma cells in type 1 response secrete antibodies. Name the other type of cell (C) in this system and describe its function. (2)

(e)   Name the three types of differentiated cell (D, E and F) in the type 2 response. (2)

(f)   Describe the function of one of the cell types you named in part (e). (1)

WJEC BI4 JUNE 2007

---

2 (a)   Complete the table, using a tick (✓) to indicate which type of immunity is shown by each of the following circumstances. (4)

	Active natural	Active artificial	Passive natural	Passive artificial
Exposure to measles				
Receiving MMR vaccine				
Receiving anti-rabies injection				
Transfer of antibodies from mother to child in breast milk				

(b)   Explain why passive immunity is not as long lasting as active immunity. (2)

(c)   The diagram demonstrates one type of immune response that occurs when the body is exposed to an antigen.

Explain what is happening during this type of response in:

(i)   Stage 1 (3)

(ii)   Stage 2 (4)

lymphocytes   antigens

stage 1   stage 2

WJEC BI4 JAN 2011

Pathogens, spread of disease and control of infection

1 (a) Antibiotics can be described as bactericidal or bacteriostatic.
State what is meant by each of these terms. (2)

(b) In a pathology laboratory a sterile Petri dish of nutrient agar was inoculated with bacteria from a swab taken from a patient with a throat infection. Four discs, each of which had been soaked in a different antibiotic, were placed onto the bacteria. The dish was incubated at 37°C. The diagram shows the appearance of the dish 24 hours later.

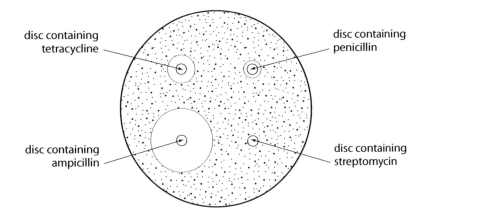

(i) Explain why there are clear zones around some of the discs containing antibiotic. (2)

(ii) Which of the antibiotics is most likely to be effective in treating the throat infection? (1)

(iii) What evidence from the laboratory test supports your suggestion? (1)

(c) Resistance to antibiotics is growing worldwide. Suggest how antibiotic resistance has arisen in bacterial populations. (3)

WJEC HB2 JUNE 2010

2 (a) Define what is meant by the term parasite. (2)

(b) The tapeworm, *Taenia solium*, is a parasite of humans. Its life cycle includes a secondary host.

(i) Name the secondary host.

(ii) Describe how the parasite is transmitted from a human to its secondary host. (1)

(iii) Explain how humans may become infected with the tapeworm. (1)

(c) *Taenia* is a parasite which lives in the human digestive tract or gut.

(i) Give one adaptation of *Taenia* which ensures that it stays in place in the gut of the host. (1)

(ii) Explain why *Taenia* is not destroyed by the secretions of the human host. (2)

(d) *Taenia* has a very high rate of reproduction. Explain the advantage of this to the parasite. (1)

WJEC HB2 JUNE 2009

Exam Practice and Technique

Exam practice and skills

How exam questions are set

WJEC AS Human Biology aims to encourage students to:

- develop their interest and enthusiasm for the subject, including developing an interest in further study and careers in the subject
- appreciate how society makes decisions about scientific issues and how the sciences contribute to the success of the economy and society
- develop and demonstrate a deeper appreciation of the skills, knowledge and understanding of How Science Works
- develop essential knowledge and understanding of different areas of the subject and how they relate to each other.

Examination questions are written to reflect the assessment objectives as laid out in the specification. Candidates must meet the following assessment objectives in the context of the content detailed in the specification.

Assessment objective AO1:
Knowledge and understanding of science and How Science Works

Candidates should be able to:

- recognise, recall and show understanding of scientific knowledge
- select, organise and communicate relevant information in a variety of forms.

47% of the questions set on the exam paper are recall of knowledge.

Assessment objective AO2:
Application of knowledge and understanding of science and How Science Works

Candidates should be able to:

- analyse and evaluate scientific knowledge and processes
- apply scientific knowledge and processes to unfamiliar situations including those relating to issues
- assess the validity, reliability and credibility of scientific information.

47% of the questions set on the exam paper include application of knowledge.

Assessment objective AO3:
How Science Works

Candidates should be able to:

- demonstrate and describe ethical, safe and skilful practical techniques and processes, selecting appropriate qualitative and quantitative methods
- make, record and communicate reliable and valid observations and measurements with appropriate precision and accuracy
- analyse, interpret, explain and evaluate the methodology, results and impact of their own and others' experimental and investigative activities in a variety of ways.

6% of the questions set on the exam paper include How Science Works.

BY1 and HB2: Written paper (1 hour 30 minutes)

The following is an approximate guide to the structure of the examination papers, BY1 and HB2:

Type of question	Marks per question	Number of questions per paper	
		BY1	HB2
Short structured	2–5	2–3	2–3
Longer structured	7–15	2–4	2–4
Essay (1 out of 2)	10	1	1
Total marks		70	70

Examination questions are written by the Principal examiner well in advance of the examination. A committee of experienced examiners discuss the quality of every question as well as the suitability of the wording.

The following is advice given in the specification:

The questions are worded very carefully so that they are clear, concise and unambiguous. Despite this, candidates tend to penalise themselves unnecessarily when they misread questions, either because they read them too quickly or too superficially. It is essential that candidates appreciate the precise meaning of each word in the question if they are to be successful in producing concise, relevant and unambiguous responses. The mark value at the end of each part of each question provides a useful guide as to the amount of information required in the answer.

Exam tips

Read the question carefully. Examiners try to make the wording of the questions as clear as possible but in the examination situation, it is all too easy to misinterpret a question. Read every word in every sentence carefully and use a highlighter pen if it helps you to focus on key words.

Understand the information

Only a certain percentage of the questions at AS are based on recall of knowledge. You may encounter unfamiliar material. It is important that you do not panic but think carefully and take your time and apply the principles that you have learnt to answer these types of question. You may also encounter a graph or table. Again, read the information carefully several times before you attempt the question.

Look at the mark allocation

Each question or part of a question is allocated a number of marks. You must make sure that if the question is worth three marks, then you must give three points to gain those marks.

Understand the instructions

Know the meaning of action words. Make sure that you are familiar with the terms below and that you understand what the examiner expects you to do.

Describe

This term may be used in a variety of questions where you need to give a step-by-step account of what is taking place. In a graph question, for example, you may be required to recognise a simple trend or pattern, then you should also use the data supplied to support your answer. At this level it is insufficient to state that the graph goes up and then flattens. You are expected to describe what goes up and by how much.

Explain

A question may ask you to describe and also explain. You will not be given a mark for merely describing what happens – a biological explanation is also needed.

Suggest

This action word often occurs at the end of a question when you are expected to put forward a sensible idea based on your biological knowledge. There may not be a definite answer to this question.

Name

This means that you must give no more than a one-word answer. You do not have to repeat the question or put your answer into a sentence. This is wasting time.

State

A brief, concise answer with no explanation.

Compare

If you are asked to make a comparison, do so. To compare the structure of an artery and a vein don't write out two separate descriptions. Make a comparative statement such as, 'an artery has a thick muscle wall and a vein has a thinner muscle wall'.

Tips about structured questions

Structured questions can be short, requiring a one-word response, or can include the opportunity for extended writing. The number of lined spaces on the exam question paper together with a mark allocation are indications of the length of answer expected and the number of points to be made. Structured questions are in several parts, usually about a common content. There is an increase in the degree of difficulty as you work your way through the question. The first part may be simple recall, perhaps defining a term, the most difficult part coming at the end of the question.

Tips about essays and diagrams

All too often candidates rush into essay questions, often writing everything they know about the topic without specifically answering the question. You should take your time reading the question carefully to discover exactly what the examiner requires in the answer. Highlight the key words then write down a plan. This will not only help you to organise your thoughts but also give you a checklist to which you can refer back while writing

your answer. In this way you will be less likely to repeat yourself, wander off the subject or miss out important points.

Consider this sample question:

'A person with long-term hypertension has an increased risk of suffering a heart attack. Discuss the methods used to monitor, diagnose and treat heart disease.'

The words to highlight are: hypertension, monitor, diagnose and treatment.

Hypertension – definition.

Monitor – methods used with explanation.

Diagnose – ECG with examples of abnormalities.

Treatment – preventative; surgical.

When you have a plan to follow, it is so much easier to organise your thoughts while writing your answer.

Should you include a diagram in your essay answer?

Where appropriate you should include well-drawn, annotated diagrams. Even in essay questions this is an excellent way of communicating biology. In fact the rubric in the essay section states: 'Any diagrams in your answer must be fully annotated'. This means that you are encouraged to include a diagram but a labelled diagram is insufficient. 'Annotate' means adding a short description of the function or relevant point about the structure of the labelled part.

Questions and answers

This part of the guide looks at student answers to examination-style questions through the eyes of an examiner. There is a selection of questions on topics in the AS specification with two sample answers – one of a high grade standard and one of a lower grade standard in each case. The examiner commentary is designed to show you how marks are gained and lost so that you understand what is required in your answers.

BY1: Basic Biochemistry and Cell Structure

page 124	Q1	Carbohydrates – structured question	*(6 marks)*
page 125	Q2	Organelle – structured question	*(9 marks)*
page 125	Q3	Active transport – structured question	*(4 marks)*
page 126	Q4	Osmosis – structured question	*(6 marks)*
page 127	Q5	Methods of transportation across cell membrane – essay	*(10 marks)*
page 129	Q6	Enzymes and inhibitors – structured question	*(12 marks)*
page 130	Q7	Enzymes – essay	*(10 marks)*
page 131	Q8	Nucleic acids – structured question	*(13 marks)*

HB2: Biodiversity and Physiology of Body Systems

page 132	Q9	Classification and antibiotics – structured question	*(6 marks)*
page 133	Q10	Stomach and ulcer – structured question	*(10 marks)*
page 134	Q11	Gaseous exchange and asthma – essay	*(10 marks)*
page 135	Q12	Capillaries – structured question	*(12 marks)*
page 136	Q13	Oxygen dissociation curve – structured question	*(8 marks)*
page 137	Q14	Chloride shift – structured question	*(6 marks)*
page 138	Q15	Hypertension and heart disease – essay	*(10 marks)*
page 139	Q16	*Salmonella* and hygiene – structured question	*(6 marks)*
page 140	Q17	Immune response – structured question	*(7 marks)*
page 141	Q18	Vaccination and tuberculosis – structured question	*(14 marks)*
page 142	Q19	Parasites – structured question	*(9 marks)*

The diagrams show part of a molecule of starch (A) and part of a molecule of cellulose (B). The hexagonal shapes represent hexose sugars.

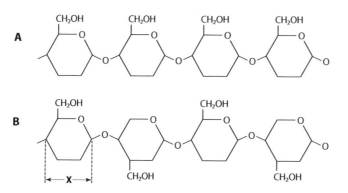

(a) Name monomer X and its form. *(1 mark)*
(b) Name the bond formed between two hexose sugars. *(1 mark)*
(c) State two structural differences between starch and cellulose. *(2 marks)*
(d) Starch is a compact storage polysaccharide. Cellulose has a structural role in plant cell wall. Describe how cellulose units are arranged in a complete molecule and how this arrangement gives cellulose a high tensile strength. *(2 marks)*

Dylan's answer

(a) Glucose ⊗ ①
(b) Glycosidic ✔
(c) One has α glucose molecules and the other has β glucose. One is coiled and the other is straight chained. ⊗②
(d) Cellulose is made up of long chains linked together like parallel strands in a rope. This makes it strong. ⊗③

Cerys's answer

(a) β glucose ✔
(b) glycosidic ✔
(c) Starch is made up of α glucose molecules while cellulose consists of β glucose. ✔ Starch is branched and cellulose is unbranched. ✔ ①
(d) Starch is made up of coiled chains; cellulose has many long, parallel straight chains linked by hydrogen bonds. ✔ The adjacent molecules are rotated by 180°. ✔ A collection of parallel chains is called a microfibril. ②

Examiner commentary

① Dylan gains no mark as he has failed to give form, β, of glucose.
② Dylan has failed to gain any marks as he has stated two correct differences but has not made a valid comparison.
③ Dylan's statement is vague. He has also failed to use the information supplied in the diagram. He has the right idea but does not express himself in the detail required at this level.

Summative comment
Dylan achieves 1 out of 6 marks.

Examiner commentary

① Cerys has provided all the points required to gain the marks. Other possible answers include, starch is coiled and cellulose is straight chained; starch has 1–4 and 1–6 linkages, cellulose 1–4 linkages only; starch has two polysaccharides, cellulose one.
② To achieve a perfect answer Cerys could have elaborated on the fact that rotating the adjacent molecules by 180° allows hydrogen bonds to be formed between –OH groups of parallel chains.

Summative comment
Cerys achieves 6 out of 6 marks.

Q&A 2

The diagram (left) shows an organelle found in a liver cell.

(a) (i) Name the organelle. *(1 mark)*

    (ii) State the function of the organelle. *(1 mark)*

    (iii) Name the structures labelled A and B in the diagram. *(2 marks)*

(b) Explain why the inner membrane is highly folded. *(2 marks)*

(c) Name the main molecule that is synthesised in this organelle. *(1 mark)*

(d) Explain why liver cells have large numbers of these organelles present. *(2 marks)*

Dylan's answer

(a) (i) Mitochondrion ✓

    (ii) Respiration ✓

    (iii) A Highly folded inner membrane ✗
        B Cytoplasm ✗ ①

(b) To increase surface area ✓ ②

(c) ATP ✓

(d) Because ATP is needed to break down substances in the liver, so mitochondria are required. ✗ ③

Examiner commentary

① Dylan has failed to learn basic labelling of the organelle.

② Dylan has gained one mark but has failed to note that the question has been allocated a second mark – an increase in surface area means that a maximum number of enzyme molecules to be attached so more ATP can be produced.

③ Dylan has not appreciated that the liver is a metabolically active organ where many energy-requiring processes, such as active transport, are taking place. Consequently, a large amount of ATP is required.

Summative comment
Dylan achieves 4 out of 9 marks

Cerys's answer

(a) (i) Mitochondrion ✓

    (ii) It is the site of respiration ✓

    (iii) A crista ✓
        B matrix ✓

(b) To increase surface area for attachment of enzymes to produce ATP ✓ ✓

(c) ATP ✓

(d) Because the liver needs a large amount of ATP (energy) ✓ in order to carry out its function. The more mitochondria it has, the more ATP is synthesised. ①

Examiner commentary

① Cerys knows that the liver needs a large amount of ATP but has not stated that there are many energy-requiring process taking place in the liver.

Summative comment
Cerys achieves 8 out of 9 marks.

Q&A 3

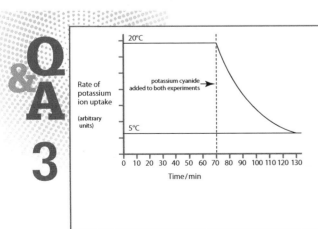

The graph shows the absorption of potassium ions by young cereal plant root hairs which were kept in aerated solutions maintained at two different temperatures. After 70 minutes potassium cyanide was added to the solutions at each temperature.

(a) How does the information given show that the root hairs take up the ions by active transport? *(3 marks)*

(b) Explain, why at low temperatures potassium uptake continues after the addition of potassium cyanide. *(1 mark)*

Dylan's answer

(a) The uptake is affected by temperature. ✓ The graph shows that adding cyanide makes the temperature go down from 20°C to 5°C. ✗ ①

(b) Because active transport is still taking place. ✗ ②

Examiner commentary

① Dylan has not studied the graph carefully, particularly with regard to the axes. Nevertheless he gains one mark perhaps more by chance than good judgement! As the uptake is affected by temperature, he should immediately have thought of the involvement of enzymes. Active transport is an energy-requiring process. Cyanide inhibits enzymes involved in respiration and no ATP is produced; thus reducing the uptake of potassium ions.

② Limited uptake does occur by diffusion as it is a passive process unaffected by cyanide.

Summative comment

Dylan achieves 1 out of 4 marks.

Cerys's answer

(a) At 70 minutes the rate of uptake of potassium is reduced considerably until it reaches 130 minutes. Then it levels out and takes place slowly. Temperature causes the reduction ✓ because aerobic respiration is inhibited by the cyanide ✓ and there is no ATP for active uptake of potassium. ✓

(b) Diffusion still takes place and this is a much slower process than active transport. ✓ ①

Examiner commentary

① Although Cerys has gained the mark, she could have stated that diffusion is a passive process and does not require energy. Uptake still occurs but at a much lower level as it is a slower process.

Summative comment

Cerys achieves 4 out of 4 marks.

The water potential of vacuolated cells is represented by the equation:

$$\Psi_{cell} = \Psi_s + \Psi_p$$

(a) Define the terms: *(2 marks)*
    (i) Osmosis   (ii) Water potential

(b) What is the water potential of pure water? *(1 mark)*

(c) Two different cells P and Q are adjacent to one another in a plant. Calculate the missing values for each cell and complete the following table (all values are in kPa). *(2 marks)*

Cell	Ψ_{cell}	Ψ_s	Ψ_p
P		-1200	+500
Q	-300		+300

(d) In which direction will water move between these two cells? *(1 mark)*

Dylan's answer

(a) (i) Osmosis is water moving from a high concentration to a low concentration across a semi-permeable membrane. ✗ ①

    (ii) Water potential is solute potential and pressure potential. ✗ ①

(b) Zero ✓

(c)

Cell	Ψ_{cell}	Ψ_s	Ψ_p
P	1700 ② ✗	-1200	+500
Q	-300	0	+300

(d) Out of P ✗ ③

Examiner commentary

① Dylan has not learnt either definition and has missed out on easy opening marks. His definition of osmosis is not acceptable at this level. He has also attempted to use the equation to give an incorrect response.

② Dylan lacks understanding of basic maths and has added together the two figures in the table.

③ As Dylan has provided the incorrect answers in the table he is unable to give the correct direction of flow.

Summative comment

Dylan achieves 1 out of 6 marks.

Cerys's answer

(a) (i) This is the movement of water from a region where it has a high water potential to a region where it has a lower water potential through a partially permeable membrane. ✓

(ii) This is the tendency for water to leave a system. ✓

(b) 0 ✓

(c)

Cell	Ψ_{cell}	Ψ_s	Ψ_p
P	-700 ✓	-1200	+500
Q	-300	-600 ✓	+300

(d) From cell Q to cell P. ✓

Examiner commentary

Cerys has a good understanding of the more difficult concept of osmosis and water potential. She has learnt her definitions and used the equation correctly to complete the table. She has also demonstrated that she understands that water moves from a high (or less negative) water potential to a low (or more negative) water potential.

Summative comment

Cerys has achieved 6 out of 6 marks.

Q&A 5

Describe the methods of transportation across a cell membrane. *(10 marks)*

Mark scheme

A candidate would be expected to give any 10 of the following 15 marking points.

① *Diffusion* ② *definition* ③ *passive process/no energy or ATP involved* ④ *facilitated diffusion* ⑤ *requires use of a carrier/channel protein* ⑥ *osmosis* ⑦ *movement of water from high to low water potential* ⑧ *active transport* ⑨ *ATP required* ⑩ *against a concentration gradient* ⑪ *protein carriers in membrane required* ⑫ *endocytosis/exocytosis* ⑬ *energy-requiring process* ⑭ *pinocytosis of liquids/phagocytosis of solids* ⑮ *invagination/fusion with membrane*

Dylan's answer

One method of transportation across a cell membrane is osmosis. ✓ ⑥ This is the net movement of water molecules from a region of high concentration to a region of low concentration across a semi-permeable membrane. ✗ ⑦ Another method is diffusion. ✓ ① This is the movement of molecules from a high concentration to a low concentration, e.g. oxygen diffuses from the high concentration in the air of the alveoli, across a membrane to the region of low concentration in the deoxygenated blood of the capillaries. ✓ ② Active transport is also a method of transportation ✓ ⑧ across a cell membrane and this method requires energy ✓ ⑨, e.g. in the root hair cells of a plant ions are actively transported into the cells from the soil solution.

Facilitated diffusion is a method of transport ✓ ④ that enables large substances, e.g. glucose, to pass across the cell membrane. These substances can fit into carrier proteins which then change shape taking the substance to the other side of the membrane. ✓ ⑪

Examiner commentary

⑦ Dylan has not used the term 'water potential' in his answer and gains no mark.

Summative comment

Dylan's answer lacks planning and organisation and his knowledge is very basic. He has also failed to mention all the answers required by the mark scheme.

Dylan achieves 7 out of 10 marks.

Cerys's answer

The methods that allow molecules to be transported across a cell membrane are diffusion, facilitated diffusion, osmosis, active transport, phagocytosis and pinocytosis.

Diffusion ✓ ① is the movement of molecules from where there are many to where there are few. ✓ ② The movement is random and will occur until equilibrium is reached. If the temperature is increased the particles have more energy, so they can therefore move faster and diffusion will occur at a higher rate. The concentration gradient is the difference in concentration between the two areas where particles are moving from and to. The distance that molecules need to travel also affects the rate because molecules move faster over smaller distances. Diffusion is a passive process. ✓ ③

Facilitated diffusion ✓ ④ is the same as diffusion, but in this case the particles being transported across the membrane travel through channel and carrier proteins. ✓ ⑤ Because the phospholipids that make up membranes have a layer of non-polar fatty acids inside them this means that only non-polar molecules can diffuse through. The larger polar molecules have to use an alternative route. Channel proteins allow these polar molecules through the membrane. Carrier proteins transport specific molecules and they can change shape to do so. Facilitated diffusion also follows the concentration gradient so it is therefore a passive process.

Osmosis ✓ ⑥ is similar to diffusion but it is specific to water. It depends on the water potential on either side of the membrane. Addition of solute molecules will lower the water potential, and areas with low water potential will draw in more water. ✗ ⑦ Osmosis is also a passive process.

Active transport ✓ ⑧ involves carrier proteins and because it takes place against a concentration gradient ✓ ⑩ it is an active process requiring energy in the form of ATP. ⑨

Phagocytosis is when a cell engulfs large molecules and brings them into a cell inside a membrane called a vesicle. Pinocytosis is the same thing but with smaller, soluble particles. ✓ ⑭ If a cell brings molecules in by this process it is called endocytosis ✓ ⑫ and if particles are being removed it is called exocytosis. Vesicles are produced at the Golgi body and released and move over to the cell membrane and fuse with it and secrete their contents out on the other side of the cell. ✓ ⑮

Examiner commentary

Cerys provides a clear opening statement covering all the methods involved in transport across a cell membrane. She then methodically defines each method in turn and describes the relevant features of each. She also describes phagocytosis, pinocytosis and exocytosis. These methods are often overlooked by candidates answering this type of question.

⑦ Although Cerys uses the term 'water potential', she has not clearly stated that osmosis is the movement of water molecules from a region of high water potential to a region of low water potential through a partially permeable membrane.

Summative comment

Cerys has produced an excellent, well-planned essay. She begins by stating the methods involved in the transport of materials across a cell membrane. She then deals with each method in sufficient detail.

Cerys achieves 10 out of 10 marks.

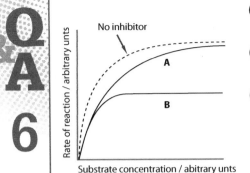

(a) Apart from the presence of inhibitors and substrate concentration, state three factors that affect the rate of an enzyme-controlled reaction. *(3 marks)*

(b) Describe how the lock and key theory can be used to explain how an enzyme breaks down a substrate molecule. *(3 marks)*

(c) The graph shows how the rate of an enzyme-catalysed reaction varies with substrate concentration when affected by a competitive inhibitor and a non-competitive inhibitor.

(i) Which line shows the competitive inhibitor? *(1 mark)*

(ii) Give a reason for your choice. *(2 marks)*

(iii) Explain how a competitive inhibitor works. *(3 marks)*

Dylan's answer

(a) PH, ✓ temperature, ✓ amount of enzyme. ✗ ①

(b) The enzyme has an active site which has a very specific shape like the lock in a door. The shape is the same shape ✗ ② as the shape of the substrate, which fits just as a key fits into a lock, forming an enzyme-substrate complex. ✓ This then breaks down to form the products.

(c) (i) A ✓

(ii) Non-competitive inhibition is not affected by the amount of substrate added. ✓ ③ With competitive inhibition, increasing the amount of substrate reduces the effect but the rate does reach its maximum eventually. ✓ ④

(iii) The inhibitor has a similar shape to the active site and substrate ✗ ⑤ and so occupies the active site of the enzyme. This prevents the substrate from binding with the active site. ✓ So no reaction takes place.

Examiner commentary

① Dylan has stated the term 'amount' rather than 'concentration' of enzyme.

② The active site and the substrate do not have the same shape, they have matching shapes, i.e. the shapes are complementary.

③ Dylan again uses the term, 'amount'. However the examiner will not penalise him again for the same error.

④ Dylan has failed to state that an enzyme-substrate complex is formed. He has also failed to consider that the greater the substrate concentration, the greater the number of collisions between substrate and enzyme and therefore the greater the chance that the substrate will enter the active site.

⑤ Dylan incorrectly states that the inhibitor has a similar shape to both substrate and active site and so fails to gain this mark.

Summative comment

Dylan achieves 7 out of 12 marks.

Cerys's answer

(a) pH, ✓ temperature, ✓ concentration of enzyme ✓

(b) The substrate fits into the active site of the enzyme ✓ because they have matching shapes. ✓ ① They form an enzyme-substrate complex and a product will be formed. ✓

(c) (i) A ✓

(ii) Non-competitive inhibition is unaffected by the concentration of substrate added. ✓ However, with competitive inhibition increasing the concentration of substrate increases the likelihood of the substrate entering the active site with the formation ✓ ② of enzyme-substrate complexes.

(iii) The inhibitor has a similar shape to that of the substrate and so occupies the active site of the enzyme in competition ✓ with the substrate. This prevents the entry of the substrate ✓ and prevents the formation of an enzyme-substrate complex. ✓

Examiner commentary

① Although Cerys has gained the mark here, she could have stated that the shape of active site and substrate are complementary to each other, rather than using the term 'matching'.

② Cerys has grasped the principle that an increase in substrate concentration increases the chance of the formation of enzyme-substrate complexes. She could have added that this is due to an increase in the likelihood of a collision of the substrate with the active site rather than the inhibitor, as more substrate molecules are present.

Cerys has an excellent grasp of this topic. She has a good understanding of how enzymes work and also how the rate of reaction is affected by inhibitors.

Summative comment

Cerys achieves 12 out of 12 marks.

Q&A 7

(a) Describe and explain why the rate of reaction of an enzyme varies with temperature.
(b) What are immobilised enzymes? Describe the advantages of their use.   *(10 marks)*

Mark scheme

A candidate would be expected to give any 10 of the following 15 marking points.

① *Enzymes are inactive at 0°C* ② *With an increase in temperature the rate of reaction increases* ③ *an increase in temperature gives molecules greater kinetic energy* ④ *molecular collisions occur resulting in formation of enzyme-substrate complexes* ⑤ *the optimum temperature is 40°C.* ⑥ *Above 40°C enzymes are denatured* ⑦ *the increased vibration of molecules causes hydrogen bonds to break / tertiary structure is altered / shape of active site is altered. (Any 5 points out of 7)*

⑧ *Enzyme molecules that are fixed / bound / trapped* ⑨ *to an inert matrix / alginate bead* ⑩ *more stable at higher temperatures* ⑪ *can tolerate wider range of pH* ⑫ *easily recovered for reuse* ⑬ *several enzymes with different pH or temperature optima can be used at one time* ⑭ *reaction more easily controlled by adding or removing enzymes* ⑮ *specific so can select one type of molecule in a mixture / can be used for rapid detection of biologically important molecules. (Any 5 points out of 8)*

Dylan's answer

As the temperature increases, so does the rate of reaction. ✓ ② Increasing the temperature means more energy ✗ ③ is available and this makes the enzyme and substrate molecules move about more. This means there are more collisions. ✗ ④ If the temperature is too high the enzyme is denatured. ✗ ⑥ An immobilised enzyme is an enzyme that is bound ✓ ⑧ in a inert matrix ✓ ⑨ e.g. gel capsules. There are many advantages of immobilised enzymes. They are cheap, they have a wide range over which they work. They have a wider range of temperature, pH ✓ ⑪, substrate concentration and enzyme concentration at which they work compared to a normal enzyme. They can also be reused easily. ✓ ⑫ They are used for testing for blood glucose level in biosensors. ✓ ⑮

Examiner commentary

③ ④ Dylan refers to energy and substrate and enzymes moving more but fails to mention the word 'kinetic' and makes no reference to enzyme-substrate complexes.

⑥ He refers to 'denaturation' but does not qualify his statement with a reference to the temperature at which this begins to occur and offers no explanation as to what denaturation means.

Summative comment

Dylan's answer to part (a) lacks detail. He fails to mention any specific temperatures and his answers are little above those expected at GCSE level. He gains maximum marks for part (b) despite poor expression.

Dylan achieves 6 out of 10 marks.

Cerys's answer

At 0°C enzymes are inactive ✓ ① but as the temperature rises, the rate of reaction increases. ✓ ② This is because the molecules gain kinetic energy and move about more. ✓ ③ This means that enzyme and substrate molecules are more likely to collide and these successful collisions result in the formation of enzyme-substrate complexes with the formation of a product. ✓ ④ 40°C is the optimum temperature for enzyme action. ✓ ⑤ Above this temperature enzymes start to denature. ✓ That is, enzyme molecules vibrate so much that the weak hydrogen bonds that hold the molecule together are broken and the tertiary structure is destroyed. ✓

Immobilised enzymes are enzymes trapped in an inert gel. ✓ ✓ ⑧⑨ They can be used over a larger range of temperatures and pH compared to normal enzymes. ✓ ⑪ This is because the inert gel helps maintain its tertiary structure. Because of the larger range of optima different immobilised enzymes can be used together. ✓ ⑬ They are good economically as the enzyme is easily separated from the product and can be reused. ✓ ⑫ Immobilised enzymes have a faster rate of reaction than ordinary enzymes and they are denatured at higher temperatures. The enzymes are used in biosensors for several different tests, one of which is blood glucose monitoring.

Examiner commentary

Cerys describes specific temperatures which affect enzymes. She refers to the temperature at which enzymes are inactive and the optimum temperature of enzyme action. She does not simply define denaturation but also describes in molecular terms how it happens.

Summative comment

Cerys has produced an excellent, concise and detailed answer.

Cerys achieves 10 out of 10 marks.

(a) Complete the table which compares DNA with messenger RNA (mRNA). *(4 marks)*

Feature	DNA	mRNA
Name of sugar		
Number of carbon atoms in sugar		
Number of polynucleotide chains in molecule		
Location in cell		

(b) The table below shows the relative amounts of the four bases in DNA taken from three sources.

Cellular source of DNA	Nitrogenous base (relative amounts)			
	Adenine	Guanine	Cytosine	Thymine
Rat muscle	28.6	21.4	21.5	28.4
Wheat seed	27.3	22.7	22.9	27.1
Yeast	31.3	18.7	17.1	32.9

(i) Explain why the relative amount of adenine is almost the same as the relative amount of thymine in each source. *(3 marks)*

(ii) Explain why the base sequence in a DNA sample taken from the bone marrow of a rat would be the same as that taken from the muscle of the same rat. *(3 marks)*

(iii) Explain how a sample of DNA from a rat sperm cell differs from that of a muscle cell from the same rat. *(3 marks)*

Dylan's answer

(a)

Feature	DNA	mRNA
Name of sugar	Pentose	Pentose ✗ ①
Number of carbon atoms in sugar	5	5 ✓
Number of polynucleotide chains in molecule	23	23 ✗
Location in cell	nucleus	Cytoplasm ✗

(b) (i) Because it all adds up to 100 so 50:50 A+G: C+T, e.g. 28.6 +21.4 = 50. ✗ ②

(ii) The DNA throughout the whole rat will be the same, no matter where the sample is taken from. ✗ ③

(iii) Because to make sperm (sex) cells it takes meiosis but meiosis ✓ makes only haploid non-identical cells, ✓ whereas mitosis would make muscle cells, for example, identical daughter cells. ✗ ④

Examiner commentary

① Dylan has made several errors in completing the table. He has failed to name the different sugars, deoxyribose and ribose present in the different nucleotides, and that DNA is double stranded whereas RNA is single stranded. He also fails to state that mRNA is present in both the nucleus and cytoplasm.

② Dylan is asking the examiner to do his thinking for him! Complementary base pairing takes place and he has used abbreviations for the bases instead of writing their names in full. He fails to answer the question which is suggesting why the figures in the table for the base pairs are not the same. This is due to experimental error.

③ Dylan has not mentioned mitosis and that replication of DNA takes place with the production of genetically identical body cells.

④ Dylan correctly states that haploid sex cells are produced by meiosis. He also would have gained a mark had he gone back to (b)(ii) and included the information about mitosis.

Summative comment
Dylan achieves 3 out of 13 marks.

Cerys's answer

(a)

Feature	DNA	mRNA
Name of sugar	Deoxyribose	Ribose ✓
Number of carbon atoms in sugar	5	5 ✓
Number of polynucleotide chains in molecule	2	1 ✓
Location in cell	Nucleus	Nucleus and cytoplasm ✓

continues over …

Cerys's answer

(b) (i) Because adenine joins with thymine in DNA by hydrogen bonds. This means that the same amount of adenine joins with the same amount of thymine. ⊗ ✓ ①

(ii) The bone marrow has the same DNA as the muscle. This is because body cells are produced by mitosis ✓ so all cells are genetically identical. ✓ ②

(iii) Because the rat's sperm is haploid ✓ as sex cells are produced by meiosis. ✓ This produces variation in each sex cell, ✓ therefore one sperm may have different DNA to the other.

Examiner commentary

① Cerys has failed to answer the question and has made a similar error to Tom. However, she has correctly named base pairs.

② Cerys has failed to state that replication of DNA takes place during mitosis.

Summative comment

Cerys achieves 10 out of 13 marks.

Q & A 9

The diagram shows the simplified structure of three different cell types A, B and C. (Not drawn to scale)

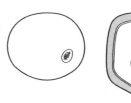 

Cell A   Cell B   Cell C

(a) State one feature that can be seen in the diagrams that enables you to decide that:
   (i) Cell B is a plant cell. *(1 mark)*
   (ii) Cell C is a prokaryotic cell. *(1 mark)*
(b) The antibiotic penicillin inhibits the formation of bacterial cell walls.
   (i) Explain how penicillin inhibits the formation of the bacterial cell wall. *(1 mark)*
   (ii) Explain how this results in the destruction of the bacteria. *(2 marks)*
   (iii) Explain why penicillin destroys bacterial cells but not human cells. *(1 mark)*

(WJEC HB2 June 2009)

Dylan's answer

(a) (i) It has a chloroplast. ⊗ ①
   (ii) It has a membrane and a cell wall. ⊗ ②
(b) (i) Penicillin makes holes in the cell wall. ⊗ ③
   (ii) This lets water in and the cell bursts. ✓⊗ ④
   (iii) Human cells do not have cell walls. ✓

Examiner commentary

Dylan has a poor understanding of the differences between the cells of different kingdoms and the effect of penicillin on cell wall formation.

① It clearly states in the stem of the question that only features that can be seen should be used in the answer.

② He fails to observe that both cells B and C have a membrane and cell wall.

③ ④ Dylan has a superficial knowledge of the effect of penicillin on the bacterial cell wall but does not express himself at the level expected.

Summative comment

Dylan achieves 2 out of 6 marks.

Cerys's answer

(a) (i) It has a vacuole. ✓
   (ii) The nucleus has no membrane around it. ✓
(b) (i) Penicillin inhibits the enzyme involved in the formation of the cell wall and blocks the cross-linking of the peptidoglycan chains of the cell wall. ✓
   (ii) This weakens the cell wall and water is taken in by the cell which swells and bursts. ✓ ✓①
   (iii) Humans use a different enzyme in the cell wall. ⊗②

Examiner commentary

Cerys has a good understanding of the differences between the cells of different kingdoms and the effect of the antibiotic, penicillin, on cell wall formation in bacteria.

① Cerys could have used the term 'osmotic lysis' to describe the take-up of water and bursting of the bacterial cell wall.

② She has failed to appreciate that humans cells do not have cell walls and so are unaffected by penicillin.

Summative comment

Cerys achieves 5 out of 6 marks.

The diagram below shows part of the wall of a human stomach.

(a) The epithelial layer secretes mucus.
State two functions of mucus. *(2 marks)*

(b) (i) A zymogen or chief cell secretes an inactive precursor of a protease.
Name this precursor. *(1 mark)*

(ii) Explain why the protease is secreted in this form. *(1 mark)*

(c) (i) Cell A secretes hydrochloric acid into the stomach.
Name the cell labelled A. *(1 mark)*

(ii) State two functions of hydrochloric acid. *(2 marks)*

(d) A peptic ulcer is an erosion of the lining of the wall of the stomach.

(i) State one major cause of peptic ulcers. *(1 mark)*

(ii) Explain how erosion of the stomach wall occurs. *(2 marks)*

(WJEC HB2 June 2009)

Diagram labels: entrances to gastric pits, submucosa, epithelial layer, gastric pit, A

Dylan's answer

(a) Mucus protects the stomach wall. ✓
It helps the food move in the gut. ✗ ①

(b) (i) Pepsin. ✗②

(ii) To break down protein. ✗ ③

(c) (i) Stomach cell. ✗④

(ii) It provides optimum pH for pepsin to work. ✓
It kills bacteria. ✓

(d) (i) Eating spicy food and food with acid in it. ✗ ⑤

(ii) The stomach lining is damaged and the acid burns into it. ✓✓ ⑥

Examiner commentary

① Dylan's answer needs to include the term 'lubricate' to gain the mark.

②③ Dylan has not understood that some enzymes need to be in an inactive form to prevent autolysis.

④ Dylan has not learnt the terms for the different cells making up the wall of the stomach.

⑤ Dylan has failed to understand the difference between the cause of an ulcer and conditions which aggravate it.

⑥ Dylan does not express himself well, nevertheless he has grasped how erosion occurs.

Summative comment
Dylan achieves 5 out of 10 marks.

Cerys's answer

(a) It protects the wall of the stomach by forming a barrier between stomach lining and gastric juice. ✓
It lubricates the food to assist in its movement within the stomach. ✓

(b) (i) Pepsinogen. ✓

(ii) In this inactive form the enzyme does not damage the stomach tissues. ✓ ①

(c) (i) Oxyntic cell. ✓

(ii) Hydrochloric acid activates pepsinogen to the active form, pepsin, and provides optimum pH for pepsin; it neutralises alkaline saliva and kills bacteria that might be taken in with food. ✓✓

(d) (i) Infection with bacteria (Helicobacter pylori). ✓ ②

(ii) A combination of increase in the production of acid and damage to the mucus lining. ✓✓

Examiner commentary

Cerys's knowledge and understanding and expression are of a high standard. This answer is worthy of an A grade. Alternative answers include:

① Enzymes can damage unprotected cells. This is called autolysis.

② Long term use of inflammatory drugs can also damage the stomach lining.

③ Other factors include drinking caffeine and eating too much spicy food. Smoking also affects the healing process.

④ Drugs to reduce stomach acid and protect stomach lining may also be prescribed.

Summative comment
Cerys achieves 10 out of 10 marks.

& Q A 11

(a) Describe how alveoli are adapted for the function of gaseous exchange. *(5 marks)*
(b) Describe the causes, symptoms and treatment of asthma. *(5 marks)*

(WJEC HB2 May 2011)

Mark scheme

A candidate would be expected to give any 10 of the following 15 marking points, with a maximum of 5 marks for each of parts (a) and (b).

(a) ① *Alveoli have thin walls* ② *short diffusion path* ③ *have a large surface area* ④ *extensive capillary network* ⑤ *to maintain diffusion gradient/movement of blood/removal of oxygen and return with carbon dioxide* ⑥ *reference to presence of surfactant* ⑦ *function of surfactant – reducing surface tension. (Any 5 out of 7.)*

(b) ⑧ *Cause – air pollution/allergen or, e.g., dust mites/fur/feathers/pollen* ⑨ *attacks of wheezing/difficulty in breathing out* ⑩ *spasms in smooth muscle walls of (smaller) bronchi/bronchioles* ⑪ *narrow airways/passageways close partially/flow of air restricted* ⑫ *inflammation of bronchioles/air passages* ⑬ *more effort required to deliver sufficient air to the lungs* ⑭ *inhaler/aerosol relax muscles (lining bronchioles)* ⑮ *steroids reduce inflammation. (Any 5 out of 8.)*

Dylan's answer

Alveoli are air sacs. There are many of these in the lungs giving a large surface area ✔ ③ for respiration. The air sacs are covered in blood capillaries ✔ ④ to bring blood to and from the lungs.

Asthma is caused by air pollution ✘ ⑧ making it difficult for people to breathe properly. ✘ ⑨ The walls of the breathing tubes like the trachea and bronchi close up so that air cannot get through properly. ✘ ✘ ⑩ ⑪ The person has to breathe really hard to get their breath. ✘ ⑬ People usually have to use an inhaler to get better. ✘ ⑭

Examiner commentary

Dylan makes no reference to the structure of the respiratory surface and the process of diffusion. He wrongly refers to gaseous exchange as 'respiration'. He mentions blood capillaries and gains a mark but does not refer to its function of maintaining a diffusion gradient or the gases involved.

⑧ His description of asthma and its causes is vague. ⑩ ⑪ He refers to 'trachea and bronchi closing up' rather than the bronchioles which lead to the alveoli. ⑭ He mentions using an inhaler but fails to describe the effect of its contents in relaxing the muscles lining the bronchioles.

Summative comment

Dylan has little knowledge or understanding of the relationship between the structure of the respiratory system and the asthma other than what he may have observed in a sufferer.

Dylan achieves 2 out of 10 marks.

Cerys's answer

The air sacs or alveoli are the gas exchange surfaces which provide a large surface area. ✔ ③ The walls are thin, ✔ ① providing a short diffusion path. ✔ ② This makes diffusion very efficient. Each alveolus is covered by many capillaries. ✔ ④ The blood flow maintains a diffusion gradient because blood is always taking oxygen away from the alveolus and returning carbon dioxide. Deoxygenated blood enters the capillaries surrounding the alveolus and oxygen diffuses out of the alveolus into the blood in the capillary. ✔ ⑤

A person with asthma has attacks of wheezing and finds difficulty in breathing. ✘ ⑨ It is thought to be caused by allergens such as dust mites, animal fur and pollen. ✔ ⑧

Attacks are brought on by spasms of the smooth muscles that lie in the walls of the bronchioles causing the passageways to partially close. ✔ ⑩ ⑪ The obstruction of these air passages means that the person has to put in more effort to deliver enough air to the lungs. ✔ ⑬ Usually the mucus membranes that line the respiratory passageways become irritated and a lot of mucus is produced. ✔ ⑫ This clogs the bronchi and bronchioles, making the attack worse. Patients are usually prescribed drugs in an aerosol. This causes the muscle lining the bronchioles to relax, so widening the airways. ✔ ⑭

Examiner commentary

⑨ A person with asthma finds difficulty in breathing out. Cerys has not made this distinction and does not gain this marking point. She could have mentioned the presence of a surfactant and its function but she has already gained full marks in this part of the question.

Summative comment

Cerys has really learnt her work and has produced an A grade answer.

Cerys achieves 10 out of 10 marks.

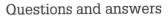

Q&A 12

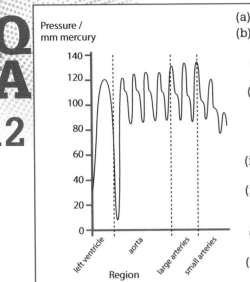

(a) Describe the function of capillaries. *(3 marks)*

(b) The diagram shows pressure changes recorded as blood flows through the heart and the arteries.

   (i) What is the value of the systolic pressure in the left ventricle? *(1 mark)*

   (ii) Fluids flow from regions of high pressure to regions of low pressure. The minimum pressure in the ventricle is lower than the minimum pressure in the aorta. Explain why blood does not flow back into the ventricle from the aorta. *(2 marks)*

   (iii) Explain what causes the left ventricle pressure to fall to a very low value. *(2 marks)*

   (iv) If the diagram had been extended to include the flow through the capillaries in the body, give two ways in which the trace would differ from the diagram. *(2 marks)*

   (v) Give one reason why the pressure in veins is lower than in capillaries. *(1 mark)*

   (vi) How is flow maintained at this low venous pressure? *(1 mark)*

Dylan's answer

(a) They are thin walled to let oxygen diffuse out to the cells. They also have a small diameter which slows down the flow of blood. ✔ ✔ ①

(b) (i) 120 ✗ ②

   (ii) Because of valves ✗ ③

   (iii) The ventricle relaxes ✗ ④

   (iv) The line would go down to a much lower level ✔ ✗ ⑤

   (v) They have a much bigger diameter ✔

   (vi) The muscles squeeze the blood up ✔

Examiner commentary

Dylan's responses lack detail and are poorly expressed. If he expanded his answers he could achieve higher marks.

① Dylan gains two marks out of the three as he has not stated that the walls are permeable.

② Dylan has failed to include the units and so gains no marks.

③ He does not name the valves or their position in the heart.

④ If Dylan had expanded his answer to state that the relaxation of the ventricle increases the volume and that the volume increases more rapidly than it is being refilled, he would have gained the mark.

⑤ Dylan has given only one reason and gains one mark.

Summative comment

Dylan achieves 5 out of 12 marks.

Cerys's answer

(a) Capillaries are thin-walled consisting of a single layer of epithelial cells. Their walls are permeable so that exchange of materials between the blood and tissues takes place by diffusion. They also have a small diameter which slows blood flow allowing time for diffusion of oxygen and glucose to take place. ✔ ✔ ✔

(b) (i) 120mmHg ✔

   (ii) There are semilunar valves at the beginning of the aorta. These close under aortic pressure preventing backflow. ✔ ✔

   (iii) The ventricle relaxes, increasing its volume. As the volume increases more rapidly than it is being refilled, the pressure decreases. ✔ ✔

   (iv) The pressure line on the graph would go down to a lower level and there would be no rhythmical fluctuation. ✔ ✔

   (v) Veins have a much larger diameter. ✔

   (vi) The massaging effect of muscles and there are valves to prevent backflow. ✔

Examiner commentary

Cerys has given detailed answers showing a good understanding of blood flow through the heart.

Summative comment

Cerys achieves 12 out of 12 marks.

Q&A 13

(a) Explain how two features of a red blood cell (erythrocyte) enable it to carry out its function. *(2 marks)*

The graph below shows the oxygen dissociation curve for normal adult human haemoglobin (A) and *Arenicola* (lugworm) haemoglobin (B). The lugworm lives in muddy sand on the seashore.

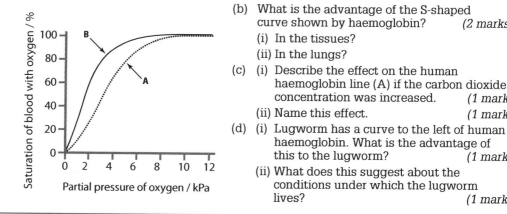

(b) What is the advantage of the S-shaped curve shown by haemoglobin? *(2 marks)*
   (i) In the tissues?
   (ii) In the lungs?

(c) (i) Describe the effect on the human haemoglobin line (A) if the carbon dioxide concentration was increased. *(1 mark)*
   (ii) Name this effect. *(1 mark)*

(d) (i) Lugworm has a curve to the left of human haemoglobin. What is the advantage of this to the lugworm? *(1 mark)*
   (ii) What does this suggest about the conditions under which the lugworm lives? *(1 mark)*

Dylan's answer

(a) The red blood cell has a large surface area to carry oxygen. ✗

It has no nucleus so has space for carrying more oxygen. ✗ ①

(b)(i) More oxygen is released ✓ ✗ ②

(ii) It is saturated at low partial pressures. ✗ ③

(c)(i) It moves to the right. ✓

(ii) Chloride shift. Bohr effect. ✗ ④

(d)(i) It is quicker at gaining oxygen. ⑤

(ii) There is less oxygen as it gets waterlogged. ✓

Examiner commentary

① Dylan's answer is incorrect as the increased surface area is for the uptake of oxygen. His second point gains no marks as the extra space is to contain haemoglobin (which in turn combines with oxygen).

② Dylan gains one mark but fails to gain the second mark as he does not explain why more oxygen is released.

③ Dylan is careless and fails to identify what is saturated.

④ Dylan is unsure and has given two answers. His first answer only is marked and is incorrect.

⑤ It is incorrect to state that haemoglobin is quicker at combining with oxygen.

Summative comment
Dylan achieves 3 out of 8 marks.

Cerys's answer

(a) The red blood cell is shaped like a biconcave disc to increase the surface area for the uptake of oxygen. ✓
   It has no nucleus so has more space for haemoglobin. ✓

(b) (i) As the partial pressure of oxygen decreases more oxygen is released. ✓

(ii) Haemoglobin is saturated at low partial pressures. ✓

(c) (i) The line moves to the right of line A. ✓

(ii) Bohr effect ✓

(d) (i) Its haemoglobin has a greater affinity for oxygen. ✓

(ii) It lives under conditions of low levels of oxygen. ✓

Examiner commentary

Cerys has an excellent understanding of this difficult topic. In (a) alternative responses are that a RBC has a flexible shape allowing the cells to squeeze through capillaries / contains haemoglobin which combines readily with oxygen.

Cerys makes correct use of terms such as 'saturation' and 'affinity'. Where carbon dioxide levels are high, as in muscle tissue, the curve shifts to the right, so haemoglobin has a greater affinity for carbon dioxide than for oxygen, and so oxygen is released to the muscle. She understands that in conditions where the partial pressure of oxygen is particularly low, as in the case of the lugworm, the curve is situated more to the left than that in the human, enabling it to load oxygen more readily.

Summative comment
Cerys achieves 8 out of 8 marks.

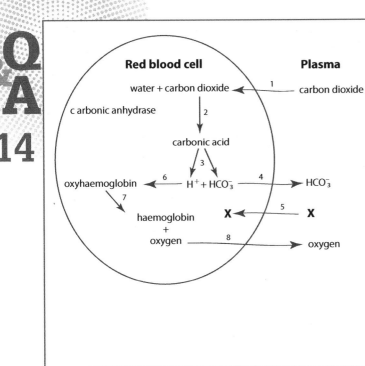

(a) State the main way that carbon dioxide is transported in the plasma. *(1 mark)*

(b) The diagram shows the role played by red blood cells in the transport of carbon dioxide. The red blood cell shown is located in respiring tissue.

(i) Carbon dioxide dissolves only very slowly in water. Inside red blood cells it dissolves quickly. Use information from the diagram to explain why carbon dioxide dissolves more quickly inside red blood cells. *(1 mark)*

(ii) Name ions X which enter the red blood cells. *(1 mark)*

(iii) Explain why ions X move into the red blood cells. *(1 mark)*

(iv) Use steps 6, 7 and 8 to explain why a high carbon dioxide concentration in tissues causes more oxygen to be released by red blood cells. *(2 marks)*

Dylan's answer

(a) As a solution Ⓧ ①

(b) (i) Because of the enzyme ✓

(ii) Chlorine Ⓧ ②

(iii) To neutralise the pH Ⓧ ③

(iv) Hydrogen ion joins with oxyhaemoglobin to give oxyhaemoglobin and releasing oxygen. Ⓧ ④

Examiner commentary

Dylan has a poor overall understanding of this process.

① Carbon dioxide is transported in three main ways, the main one being hydrogen carbonate.

② Chlorine fails to gain a mark, he should state chloride ions

③ Dylan has become confused with the dissociation of carbonic acid into hydrogen ions and hydrogen carbonate and thinks that the overall pH of the cell is affected. In fact as hydrogen carbonate ions move out, chloride ions move in to maintain electrochemical neutrality.

④ The release of hydrogen ions creates more acidic conditions in the red blood cell which causes oxyhaemoglobin to dissociate releasing oxygen with the formation of HHb. The oxygen diffuses out to the tissues.

Summative comment

Dylan achieves 1 out of 6 marks.

Cerys's answer

(a) As sodium hydrogen carbonate ✓

(b) (i) Because of the enzyme, carbonic anhydrase ✓

(ii) Chloride ions ✓

(iii) To counteract the negatively charged hydrogen carbonate ions that have moved out. ✓

(iv) Carbonic acid dissociates into hydrogen ions and bicarbonate ions. The acid condition causes the release of oxygen. Ⓧ Ⓧ ①

Examiner commentary

① Cerys has not used the information provided in the diagram to explain that hydrogen ions provide the conditions for the oxyhaemoglobin to dissociate into oxygen and haemoglobin. The hydrogen ions combine with haemoglobin to form haemoglobinic acid. The dissociated oxygen is released from the red blood cell to the tissues.

Summative comment

Cerys achieves 4 out of 6 marks.

Q&A

15

A person with long-term hypertension has an increased risk of suffering a heart attack. Discuss the methods used to monitor, diagnose and treat heart disease. *(10 marks)*

(WJEC HB2 June 2010)

Mark scheme

A candidate would be expected to give any 10 of the following 15 marking points.

Monitoring: ① Measuring blood pressure/using a sphygmomanometer ② indication of healthy B.P. 120/75 ③ lower figure/diastolic pressure indicates high resistance in the arteries to the flow of blood ④ build-up of material/atheroma increases resistance to blood flow/atherosclerosis.

Diagnosis: ⑤ Electrocardiogram/ECG ⑥ shows electrical activity taking place in the heart muscle ⑦ irregularities (compared with normal activity) indicate cardiac disorders ⑧ example arrhythmia.

Treatment: Preventative – ⑨ reduce blood pressure by lifestyle changes – reducing body weight and taking regular exercise/cut out smoking ⑩ other high risk factors – smoking, high salt intake, excess alcohol consumption ⑪ daily dose of aspirin – reduces ability of blood to clot. Heart attack – ⑫ clot-busting drugs/streptokinase ⑬ angioplasty ⑭ inflation of balloon to restore lumen to 'normal' diameter ⑮ open heart surgery/coronary by-pass.

Dylan's answer

Hypertension means having a high blood pressure. This can be measured by taking a person's pulse. If it is going too fast even when sitting down then a person might get a heart attack. This is very serious. A person who is overweight, smokes, drinks and watches television a lot is more likely to get a heart attack. They will then have an operation called 'open heart surgery'. ✓⑮

Examiner commentary

Dylan has a very superficial knowledge about heart disease. He uses 'layman's' terms and is well below the standard required at this level. It is apparent that he is not used to 'planning essays' and has not used the key terms provided in the stem of the question to help him.

Summative comment

Dylan achieves 1 out of 10 marks.

Cerys's answer

A person having a high diastolic pressure all the time even when at rest is suffering from hypertension. They have an increased risk of suffering a heart attack and stroke.

People can reduce the risk by having a healthy diet, taking regular exercise, avoiding stress and not smoking. ✓⑩ If their blood pressure stays high despite a change in lifestyle, drugs are prescribed until the condition is under control. Blood pressure can be measured using a sphygmomanometer. ✓① A young, healthy adult's blood pressure is around 120/75. ✓② A fat deposit, called an atheroma, builds up from cholesterol taken up from the blood causing the lumen of the blood vessels to become much narrower. The atheroma increases the resistance to blood flow. ✓④ This condition is called atherosclerosis. If it occurs in a coronary artery, a pain (called angina), is experienced during exercise. Atherosclerosis increases the risk of a blood clot forming in the artery. If this happens in a coronary artery it is known as a coronary thrombosis. If blood is prevented from passing through a coronary artery the heart muscle it supplies may stop beating. This is called a myocardial infarction or heart attack.

If a person is suspected of having heart disease they are given an electrocardiogram or ECG. ✓⑤ A chart shows the electrical activity taking place in the heart muscle ✓⑥ and any irregularities indicate cardiac disorders ✓⑦ such as arrhythmia. ✓⑧

If a person has a heart attack they are given 'clot bursting drugs', such as streptokinase. ✓⑫ If heart surgery is needed this can be carried out in a number of different ways. Angioplasty ✓⑬ does not involve opening the chest cavity. The patient is given a general anaesthetic then a small balloon is threaded into the partly blocked coronary artery though a tube. It is then inflated and as the balloon expands it presses against the atheroma and makes tears in it. ✓⑭ This allows the artery wall to be pushed outwards by the pressure of the blood, restoring the lumen to its normal width. The balloon is deflated and removed. Other heart operations involve 'open-heart' surgery where the chest cavity is cut open. Coronary bypass surgery is used when a patient's coronary arteries are badly blocked. ✓⑮

Examiner commentary

Cerys has produced a high quality, detailed answer. She uses the scientific terms correctly and her thoughts are expressed clearly and concisely.

Summative comment

Cerys achieves 10 out of 10 marks.

Q & A

16

Salmonella bacteria affect the gut lining causing diarrhoea and vomiting. There is usually an interval of several hours between ingesting salmonella and the appearance of symptoms.

(a) (i) Explain why there is a time interval before the appearance of symptoms. *(1 mark)*

    (ii) Explain the cause of the symptoms. *(2 marks)*

(b) Aled was employed working in the kitchen of a restaurant. Before starting work he was instructed in basic food hygiene. Explain how each of the following minimises the risk of salmonella food poisoning:

    (i) Using disposable dish-cloths. *(1 mark)*

    (ii) Storing food in cool conditions in the refrigerator. *(1 mark)*

    (iii) Keeping raw meat at the bottom of the refrigerator and cooked meat at the top. *(1 mark)*

(WJEC HB2 June 2010)

Dylan's answer

(a) (i) It takes time for the food to pass to the various parts of the gut. ✗①

    (ii) Bacteria produce poisons. ✗✗②

(b) (i) Bacteria might be transferred from an old cloth. ✓

    (ii) Bacteria don't reproduce in the cold. ✗③

    (iii) They should not be next to each other because they might come in contact with each other. ✗④

Examiner commentary

① Dylan has not appreciated that it takes time for bacteria in the contaminated food to multiply.

② At this level Dylan would be expected to use the correct term for 'poisons'. He has also failed to state the effect that toxins have on the gut wall.

③ Dylan does not understand that bacteria still reproduce at 5°C but more slowly.

④ He has the right idea but does not state that the food may be contaminated with bacteria and that direct contact may not be needed for transmission as contaminated blood may drip onto the cooked meat if placed above.

Summative comment
Dylan achieves 1 out of 6 marks.

Cerys's answer

(a) (i) It takes time for the bacteria to multiply so the symptoms don't appear straightaway. ✓

    (ii) Bacteria produce poisons called toxins. These irritate the lining of the gut. ✓✓

(b) (i) Bacteria might be picked up on the cloth which might have food on it and reproduce. ✓

    (ii) The temperature in a fridge is normally about 5°C. At this temperature reproduction of bacteria is slower because the enzymes are less active. ✓

    (iii) If the raw meat was at the top, blood containing bacteria could drip onto cooked food. ✓

Examiner commentary

Cerys has correctly used scientific concepts to illustrate her answers.

Summative comment
Cerys achieves 6 out of 6 marks.

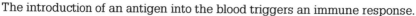

Q & A

17

The introduction of an antigen into the blood triggers an immune response.

(a) What is meant by the terms antibody and antigen? *(2 marks)*

(b) The Rubella virus infects human cells and causes the disease known as German measles. The graph shows the effect of immunising a child against Rubella. An initial injection is given and this is followed by a booster injection four weeks later.

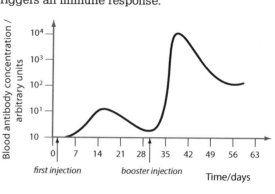

(i) Use the information in the graph to describe two differences in the response to the first and second exposure to the antigen. *(2 marks)*

(ii) Explain why there is a difference in the response. *(1 mark)*

(c) Vaccination against smallpox has been effective in eliminating the disease but this method of protection against influenza virus has only limited success. Explain the difference. *(2 marks)*

(WJEC HB2 June 2009)

Dylan's answer

(a) An antigen is a substance that brings about an immune response. ✓ An antibody is produced in response to an antigen. ✓

(b) (i) There is a delay after the first injection and the graph goes up a bit but after the booster is given the graph goes up much higher and straightaway. ✓✗ ①

(ii) The body has come already come in contact with the virus and so responds quicker. ✗②

(c) More vaccines have been used against smallpox and so it has been wiped out. Scientists are still researching new vaccines against flu. ✗✗ ③

Examiner commentary

① Dylan has failed to study the graph thoroughly before attempting the question. Although he has noted the 'latent period' after the first injection is administered, he has not related this to the increase in antibodies produced and the greater production of antibodies in the second response.

② Dylan has failed to appreciate that memory cells are produced after first contact with an antigen.

③ Dylan has no knowledge of the ability of viruses to mutate and that the smallpox virus has a low mutation rate and so produces few antigenic types. Whereas the influenza virus mutates frequently and new vaccines have to be developed to be effective against new strains of the virus.

Summative comment

Dylan's knowledge is limited to knowing the difference between antigens and antibodies. He is unable to analyse information supplied in the graph. His weak knowledge limits his ability to access the marks.

Dylan achieves 3 out of 7 marks.

Cerys's answer

(a) An antigen is a non-self molecule that stimulates the production of antibodies. ✓ An antibody is a special protein called an immunoglobulin produced in response to an antigen. It is also specific to a particular antigen. ✓

(b) (i) After the first exposure there is a delay of about 6 days before antibodies are produced but after the booster is given they are produced immediately and in far greater quantity. ✓✓ ①

(ii) Memory cells which remain after the first response cause a rapid response. ✓

(c) The virus causing smallpox has a low mutation rate whereas the influenza virus mutates frequently so there are many different strains of influenza virus. These are called antigenic types. The vaccine is only effective against a particular strain. ✓✓

Examiner commentary

① Cerys could have also stated that antibodies remain in the blood for longer during the secondary response.

Summative comment

Cerys has an excellent grasp of this topic. Cerys achieves 7 out of 7 marks.

Read the following passage and answer the questions that follow.

Tuberculosis (TB) is an infectious disease that is endemic in many countries. The pathogen is a bacterium, *Mycobacterium tuberculosis*.

One way of contracting the disease is by drinking milk from infected cows, which form a reservoir of infection. Dairy herds are regularly tested for the disease. This, together with the fact that most people are vaccinated against the disease, has restricted its spread.

Before vaccination, a test is carried out to determine whether the individual already has immunity to TB. The most common test is the Heaf test by which small needles are pressed onto the skin of the forearm. The needles carry tiny amounts of tuberculin protein, which is derived from the bacteria. If the test is positive (a raised red reaction on the skin) then the individual has previously been in contact with the bacterium and has already developed immunity. If no reaction is seen, immunisation is given as the BCG vaccination, the vaccine containing a live but weakened form of the pathogen.

People with the disease are treated with antibiotics. If, however, these drugs are mismanaged or misused then multi-drug-resistant strains of the bacterium develop.

(a) State what is meant by each of the following terms: *(5 marks)*
   (i) Infectious disease; (ii) endemic; (iii) pathogen; (iv) reservoir; (v) antibiotic.

(b) (i) Explain why a reaction to the Heaf test indicates that a person already has immunity to TB. *(2 marks)*

   (ii) State the type of immunity provided by the BCG vaccination. *(2 marks)*

   (iii) Describe the events that take place in the body's immune system after the vaccination has been administered. *(5 marks)*

(WJEC BI4 Jan 2008)

Dylan's answer

(a) (i) A disease that can be passed on. ⊗①

   (ii) A disease that is common in an area. ⊗ ②

   (iii) An organism that causes harm to humans. ⊗ ③

   (iv) A place where a disease, is normally found. ⊗ ④

   (v) A drug which fights bacteria. ⊗⑤

(b) (i) Antibodies are already present in the body to act against the antigens. ✔⊗ ⑥

   (ii) Artificial. ✔⊗ ⑦

   (iii) Antibodies recognise the antigen and more antibodies are made to fight against the antigens. The next time the person gets the disease he will have antibodies already present to fight the disease quicker. ⊗⊗⊗⊗⊗ ⑧

Examiner commentary

① to ⑤ Dylan has not learnt definitions and has failed to gain any marks. His responses are vague and inaccurate, well below the level expected.

⑥ He gains a mark but fails to state why the antibodies are already present in the body.

⑦ Dylan has not included the term 'active' indicating that memory cells are produced.

⑧ His response is that of a weak GCSE candidate.

Summative comment

Dylan achieves 2 out of 14 marks.

Cerys's answer

(a) (i) A disease that can be transferred from one organism to another. ✔

   (ii) A disease that is always present at a low level in an area. ✔

   (iii) An organism, such as a bacterium or virus, that causes disease. ✔

   (iv) A place where a pathogen is normally found. ✔

   (v) A chemical produced by microbes that affects the growth of bacteria. ✔

(b) (i) The individual has a reaction because the immune system has responded by causing localised inflammation. The individual already has antibodies present because she has previously been exposed to the pathogen and these antibodies are acting against the antigen applied in the test. ✔✔

   (ii) Artificial active. ✔✔

   (iii) B lymphocytes specific for the antigen have multiplied by mitosis to produce plasma cells and memory cells. The plasma cells produce antibodies and the memory cells remain in the blood. If the individual becomes infected again, antibodies are produced immediately and in a large quantity. ✔✔✔✔✔

Examiner commentary

Cerys has learnt her definitions and has gained the factual knowledge mark. She also has an excellent understanding of immunisation.

Summative comment

Cerys achieves 14 out of 14 marks.

Q&A 19

(a) Describe two ways in which each of the following parasites is able to survive the hostile environment within the human body:

(i) The pork tapeworm *Taenia solium*. *(2 marks)*

(ii) The malarial parasite *Plasmodium*. *(2 marks)*

(b) The maps show the incidence of malaria and the annual rainfall in Africa.

(i) Describe the relationship between the incidence of malaria and the annual rainfall in Africa. *(1 mark)*

(ii) Suggest an explanation for this relationship. *(2 marks)*

(c) Giving a different reason each time, outline how each of the following methods prevents the transmission of malaria: *(2 marks)*

(i) Stocking ponds with fish.

(ii) Spraying oil on the surface of ponds.

(WJEC HB2 June 2010)

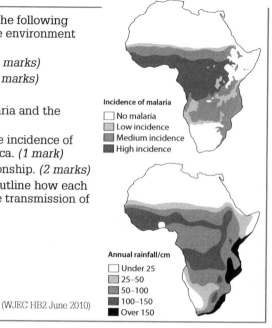

Incidence of malaria
- ☐ No malaria
- ▨ Low incidence
- ▨ Medium incidence
- ■ High incidence

Annual rainfall/cm
- ☐ Under 25
- ▨ 25–50
- ▨ 50–100
- ▨ 100–150
- ■ Over 150

Dylan's answer

a) (i) The tapeworm has hooks and suckers and a thick cuticle. ⊗⊗ ①

(ii) Malaria lives inside the liver. ⊗⊗ ②

b) (i) The more it rains the more people get malaria. ⊗③

(ii) Malaria lives in swamps where mosquitoes breed. Malaria is spread by mosquitoes. ✓✓ ④

c) (i) Fish feed on mosquitoes. ⊗ ⑤

(ii) This kills the mosquitoes that land on the water. ⊗⑥

Examiner commentary

① Although Dylan correctly states the adaptations of the tapeworm to its hostile environment, he fails to give the functions of the adaptations.

② Dylan makes the common error of referring to the parasite as 'malaria' which is the disease caused by *Plasmodium*. He also fails to give any details of its adaptations.

③ Dylan's expression is weak and he does not use the terms provided with the maps to formulate his statement. He suggests that the more it rains the worse the disease gets.

④ Although Dylan states that the 'disease' malaria 'lives in swamps', he is not penalised again for this error.

⑤ The fish feed on mosquito larvae not the adult.

⑥ The larval forms of the mosquito live in the water and breathe through breathing tubes at the surface, which are clogged by the oil

Summative comment

Dylan has little detailed knowledge of the life cycle of the mosquito and makes vague and incorrect responses.

Dylan achieves 2 out of 9 marks.

Cerys's answer

(a) (i) <u>Taenia</u> has suckers and hooks for attachment to the gut wall. ✓

It has a thick cuticle. This prevents digestion by the host's enzymes and protects it from the acid pH in the stomach. ✓ ①

(ii) <u>Plasmodium</u> lives inside host cells for some of its life cycle so its antigens are not exposed to attack by the immune system of the host. It also has rapidly changing surface antigens and so has different antigenic types. ✓✓

(b) (i) The higher the rainfall the greater the incidence of malaria. ✓

(ii) High rainfall linked to water in swamps and lakes where mosquitoes breed. The mosquito acts as a vector of the malarial parasite transmitting the disease when the female mosquito feeds on the blood of a human. ✓✓

(c) (i) This is an example of biological control. Fish called guppies are introduced to the ponds to feed on mosquito larvae which live in the water. ✓

(ii) Larvae are killed when oil clogs their breathing tubes. ✓

Examiner commentary

① An alternative answer is that 'inhibitors are present on surface of segments to prevent digestion by enzymes'.

Summative comment

Cerys is an A grade student.

Cerys achieves 9 out of 9 marks.

Quickfire answers

BY1 Basic Biochemistry and Cell Structure

① Condensation – when two monosaccharides join to form a disaccharide with the elimination of water and the formation of a glycosidic bond.

Hydrolysis – the addition of water to a disaccharide resulting in the formation of two monosaccharides.

② Lactose – disaccharide – plants and animals – energy

Cellulose – polysaccharide – plants – structural

Glucose – monosaccharide – plants and animals – energy

Glycogen – polysaccharide – animals – energy store

③ Broken down to form one molecule of glycerol and three molecules of fatty acid with the elimination of water and the breaking of an ester bond.

④ When oxidised, lipids provide more than twice as much energy as carbohydrates. If fat is stored, the same amount of energy can be provided for less than half the mass. It is therefore a lighter storage product.

⑤ Water produced from the oxidation of food is called metabolic water. When water is scarce a camel can metabolise fats.

⑥ A triglyceride has three fatty acids, no phosphate group and is non-polar.

A phospholipid has two fatty acids, one phosphate group and a hydrophilic head and a hydrophobic tail.

⑦ Hydrophilic heads.

⑧ 1. Intrinsic protein
2. Phospholipid

⑨ Peptide
Hydrogen
Disulphide
Ionic

⑩ Insulin – globular
Collagen – fibrous
Keratin – fibrous
Lysozyme – globular

⑪ A polar molecule carries an unequal distribution of electrical charge. The oxygen end has a slightly negative charge and the hydrogen end of the molecule has a slightly positive charge.

⑫ Pondskater – high surface tension.
Water has a maximum density at $4°C$ so ice floats forming an insulating layer for animals below.
Sweating – high latent heat.

⑬ 1. To allow chemical reactions to take place in solution.
2. To allow light to pass through for photosynthesis.

⑭ Core of nucleic acid
Protein coat

⑮ 1. Ribosome
2. Golgi body
3. Mitochondrion
4. Nucleolus

⑯ 1. Mitochondria
2. Chloroplast
3. Endoplasmic reticulum

⑰ Chloroplasts
Cell wall
Large permanent vacuole

⑱ Kidney – organ
Epithelium – tissue
Muscle – tissue
Sperm – cell

⑲ Extrinsic proteins occur on the surface of the bilayer or partly embedded in it. Intrinsic proteins extend across both layers.

⑳ Vitamin A is fat soluble and freely passes through the lipid bilayer. Large molecules such as glucose are insoluble in lipids and cannot pass through the non-polar centre of the phospholipid bilayer. Intrinsic proteins assist glucose to pass in and out of the cell by facilitated diffusion.

㉑ Larger surface area; thin.

㉒ Increase in kinetic energy of molecules results in an increase in rate.

㉓ Carrier proteins are involved in facilitated diffusion.

㉔ Both use carrier proteins; active transport requires energy/ATP; occurs against a concentration gradient.

㉕ Muscle contraction
Nerve impulse transmission
Protein synthesis
Uptake of minerals by roots

㉖ CAB.

㉗ When the cell membrane just pulls away from the cell wall.

㉘ A rise in temperature increases the kinetic energy of molecules. In an enzyme-catalysed reaction the enzyme and substrate molecules collide more often in a given time so that the rate of reaction increases.

㉙ When all the active sites are filled, a point is reached when all the active sites are working as fast as possible. The rate of reaction is at a maximum and the addition of more substrate will have no effect on the rate of reaction, which levels off.

㉚ pH
Substrate concentration
(Not temperature)

㉛ In competitive inhibition the inhibitor occupies the active site of the enzyme.
In non-competitive inhibition the inhibitor attaches to a site other than the active site.

㉜ Increasing the substrate concentration reduces the effect of the competitor inhibitor.
In non-competitive inhibition the rate of reaction is unaffected.

㉝ The rate of reaction of the immobilised enzyme is greater between $0°C$ and $40°C$; the optimum temperature of the immobilised enzyme covers a wider range; the immobilised enzyme begins to denature at a higher temperature/the free enzyme is completely denatured at $60°C$ whereas the immobilised enzyme is denatured at $80°C$; the immobilised enzyme is more active at all temperatures except $40°C$.

HB2 Biodiversity and Physiology of Body Systems

㉞ Accuracy
Quantitative result
Measures low concentrations

㉟ Cytoplasm only – ribosomal RNA and transfer RNA
Nucleus and cytoplasm – mRNA

㊱ DNA – sugar is deoxyribose, double stranded, thymine base
RNA sugar is ribose, single stranded, uracil base

㊲ Replication of DNA
Cell increases in size
Organelles produced replacing those lost during previous division
ATP production

㊳ Production of large numbers of identical offspring in a relatively short period of time, e.g. bulbs, tubers and runners.

㊴ Mitosis – one division, chromosome number unchanged, no crossing over, daughter cells genetically identical.
Meiosis – two divisions, chromosome number halved, crossing over occurs, daughter cells genetically different.

㊵ Crossing over
Independent assortment
Mixing of two parental genotypes

① Loss of habitat, overhunting by humans, competition from introduced species, deforestation.

② A group of organisms which can interbreed to produce fertile offspring.

③ The binomial system uses an international language so that scientists are presented with precise identification worldwide.

④ They do not possess chlorophyll.

⑤ *Homo sapiens*.

⑥ The oldest rocks, and therefore the earliest fossils, are contained in the lowest layers.

⑦ Fossil evidence suggests that primates appeared around 60–65 million years ago.

⑧ Neanderthals had slightly heavier brow ridges and less pronounced chins, but their brains, on average, were slightly larger than ours.

⑨ Manual dexterity, large brain, speech, use of fire, able to manipulate the environment, able to make clothing and shelter.

⑩ The species has evolved to a point where no further change takes place; the species does not evolve any further.

⑪ The multiregional model suggests that modern humans evolved in many parts of the Earth from regional descendants of *Homo erectus*, who migrated from Africa between 1 and 2 mya. The 'out of Africa' model suggests that only the African descendants of *Homo erectus* gave rise to modern humans.

⑫ The greater the similarity of the sequences of bases in DNA, the closer the organisms are related in terms of evolution.

⑬ The breakdown of large insoluble molecules into soluble molecules by means of enzymes.

⑭ The passage of soluble/digested food through the intestine/gut wall into the bloodstream.

⑮ Serosa; muscle; submucosa; mucosa.

⑯ Carbohydrate: glucose; fats: fatty acids and glycerol; proteins: amino acids.

⑰ To prevent the active form of the enzyme from damaging the stomach tissues.

⑱ Bile emulsifies fats, i.e. breaks down fat into smaller droplets having a larger surface area for more efficient enzyme action. Bile also neutralises acid from the stomach.

Mucus lubricates and provides protection to the gut wall.

⑲ Endopeptidase, amylase and lipase.

⑳ Endopeptidase breaks bonds in the middle of the polypeptide chain, whereas exopeptidase acts at the ends of a chain. The production of many shorter chains provides more exposed ends for exopeptidase to act on.

㉑ Glucose and amino acids pass into the capillary network that supplies each villus.
Fatty acids and glycerol are passed into the lacteal.

㉒ Lipids are used for membranes and hormones.

㉓ Blood in the faeces.

㉔ Water is absorbed from the colon.

㉕ There is a reduction in surface area for absorption resulting in a reduced uptake as minerals and vitamins are not absorbed as efficiently.

㉖ An excess of processed foods containing refined low fibre flour should be avoided. The treatment of diverticulosis involves eating a high fibre diet.

㉗ Infection with *Helicobacter pylori*; long-term use of anti-inflammatory drugs.

㉘ Eating spicy food; drinking caffeine and alcohol; stress.

㉙ Antibiotics; drugs to reduce stomach acid; drugs to protect the lining of the stomach.

㉚ Surface area; membrane thickness; permeability; concentration gradient; temperature.

㉛ An increase in size is associated with a higher metabolic rate and a greater requirement for oxygen for respiration. There is also a smaller surface area to volume ratio so oxygen needs to diffuse over a greater distance.

㉜ Alveoli; bronchioles; bronchus; trachea.

㉝ Preventing trachea collapsing during inspiration.

㉞ Flow rate is decreased as air is expelled; more difficult to breathe out; takes longer to complete a breath. This is because the constriction or inflammation of the lining of the bronchi restricts flow.

㉟ The surface area of the emphysema sufferer is reduced. This means that fewer molecules of oxygen can diffuse at any one time; rate of diffusion is reduced.

36 As a non-smoker gets older there is a reduction in forced expiration volume and at age 75 it is reduced by 25%. For a smoker there is a much greater reduction in FEV_1 and is reduced by 90% at age 75.

37 Biconcave in shape – increases surface area for the absorption of more oxygen.

No nucleus – more room to contain haemoglobin.

38 Red blood cells have no nucleus; white blood cells have a nucleus.

Red blood cells are smaller than white blood cells.

39 Blood of group O contains no agglutinogens on the red blood cells and can be given to all other blood groups.

40 Individuals of blood group AB have no agglutinogens in their plasma and can receive restricted amounts of either blood group A or blood group B.

41 A Rhesus negative mother who has a Rhesus positive baby is given an injection of anti-Rhesus antibodies after the birth to destroy any Rhesus positive cells that have entered her circulation.

42 Tiredness, feeling weak, sometimes having dizzy spells and feeling faint. As the condition becomes more severe additional symptoms include shortness of breath, palpitations and headaches. In addition the patient looks pale.

43 Red meat, eggs, milk, spinach, etc.

44 A blood transfusion.

45 To withstand the pressure where blood is pumped from the left ventricle of the heart.

To maintain the pressure that is reduced by friction when blood flows through the blood vessels.

46 To slow the flow of blood to give time for the diffusion of substances at the capillaries.

47 To generate more pressure as it has to pump the blood further (all round the body).

48 There will be a greater force generated from the base as the whole muscle contracts, also ensuring that the compartment is completely emptied.

49 Smoking; a diet high in unsaturated fat; lack of exercise.

50 The coronary artery supplies the heart muscle with oxygen; glucose for respiration.

51 A fat deposit builds up; lines the wall of the blood vessel. The fat is taken up from cholesterol in the blood.

52 Blood, carrying oxygen and glucose, is prevented from passing through the artery and the heart muscle is not being able to contract, resulting in a heart attack.

53 Ventricles contract; systole.

54 A small balloon is threaded into the partially blocked artery and when inflated it expands against the atheroma, making tears in it and restoring the lumen to its normal width.

55 Angioplasty widens the lumen and relieves the resistance to blood flow.

56 Oxyhaemoglobin.

57 The foetus curve is more to the left; haemoglobin combines more readily with oxygen. It has a greater affinity with oxygen and so takes up oxygen from the mother's haemoglobin.

58 To preserve electrochemical neutrality.

59 Hydrostatic pressure and water potential/osmosis.

60 Venous and lymphatic.

61 Distended abdomen and swelling of the feet due to oedema.

62 Acts as a barrier to prevent pathogen entry; natural skin flora act as competition against pathogens; pH of skin prevents growth of pathogens.

63 Lysosomes.

64 Immunoglobulins.

65 Thymus gland.

66 T lymphocyte

67 No memory cells are produced.

68 Once the antigen is detected by B lymphocytes these activated cells divide rapidly by mitosis forming a clone of plasma cells.

69 The organism causing smallpox has a low mutation rate, whereas the influenza virus has many different antigenic types. A vaccine is effective against one particular strain. Immunity to influenza is therefore short-lived as the virus mutates so frequently.

70 It can be a long time before symptoms show; the immune system may still be functioning; there may be a long latent period.

71 Virus destroys T helper cells, B cells not stimulated and fewer antibodies produced. Fewer T killer cells; pathogens not destroyed and numbers increase. Antiviral drugs slow onset of AIDS.

72 An endemic disease is always present at a low level, whereas with an epidemic there is a significant increase in the usual number of cases of a disease.

73 The recommended cooking time would be insufficient to kill bacteria if the centre of the bird remained frozen.

74 It takes time for the bacteria to multiply. Bacteria produce toxins which irritate the lining of the gut.

75 The time interval between infection and the development of symptoms.

76 Due to the number of antigenic types and the regular emergence of new ones, they are not always effective.

77 Toxins from the cells of the parasite accumulate in the bloodstream, causing severe bouts of fever.

78 The oil is taken into the breathing tubes of the larvae which live in the water and kills them.

79 Ampicillin.

80 Tetracycline.

81 The wall is weakened and water enters by osmosis resulting in the bacterium swelling. As more and more water enters, the cell bursts. This is called osmotic lysis.

82 Resistance is the ability of an organism to survive exposure to a dose of the poison which would normally be lethal to it.

83 MRSA.

84 Snail.

85 The infected snail larvae penetrate the skin of areas exposed when humans wash or go fishing.

86 Pig.

87 Extremes of pH; the immune system of the host; digestive enzymes; constant flow of digestive juices.

88 Hooks and suckers; thick cuticle.

89 To overcome the problem of transfer to another host; to increase the chance of some of the offspring reaching the new host.

Exam practice answers
BY1

Biochemistry

1. (a) nitrogen (not N)
   (b) (i) heat/boil with Benedict's solution: orange/red (precipitate) (accept green/yellow)
      (ii) A
   (c) C
   (d) (i) D
      (ii) saturated: no double bonds; all carbon atoms attached to two hydrogen atoms; fewer hydrogen atoms in unsaturated (or converse)

2. (a)(i) hydrogen/H
      (ii) binds cellulose (molecules) together/forms microfibrils; strengthens the wall/cellulose fibres are strong/gives structural stability; can resist turgor/osmotic pressure
   (b) (i) condensation/polymerisation
      (ii) has amino acids added/some –OH groups replaced by amino acids (to form a mucopolysaccharide)
      (iii) component of (exo)skeleton – strong/waterproof/light
   (c) (i) glycogen
      (ii) starch/amylose/amylopectin

3. (a) H/water
   (b) F/calcium or G/phosphate
   (c) I/sucrose
   (d) A/magnesium
   (e) D/cellulose
   (f) G/phosphate

Cell structure and organisation

1. (a) A: outer membrane; B inter-membrane space; C: crista; D: matrix
   (b) to increase surface area; for chemical reactions of respiration to take place
   (c) ATP

2. (a) (i) A: nucleolus; B: ribosomes; C: mitochondrion; D: Golgi body/apparatus; E: smooth endoplasmic reticulum (not SER)
      (ii) structure present: B; structure absent: A/C/D/E
   (b) B: for protein synthesis; C: for ATP production/energy release

3. (a) bacterial cell: prokaryote; plant cell: eukaryote
   (b) A: mesosome; B: chromosome; C: plasmodesmata

   (c) H is surrounded by a nuclear membrane; B is not
        H contains chromatin; B does not
        DNA in B lies free in the cytoplasm; in H the DNA is not free
   (d) D: photosynthesis/converting light energy into chemical energy
        E: exocytosis/secretion of glycoprotein/protein/synthesis of steroids/making lysosomes/packaging or transport with details
        F: protein synthesis
        G: ATP production/energy production.

Membranes and transport

1. (a) A: cell/plasma membrane; B: cell wall; C: cytoplasm; D: tonoplast/vacuolar membrane; E: vacuole; F: plasmodesmata
   (b) diffusion; osmosis; active transport; facilitated diffusion
   (c) cytoplasm/vacuole shrinks; gaps between cell wall and cytoplasm
   (d) (i) the tendency for water molecules to leave a system
      (ii) zero
      (iii) P: -700 kPa Q: -600 kPa
      (iv) from Q to P; into P

2. (a) A: phospholipid head/hydrophilic head/phosphate/polar group
        B: hydrophobic tails/fatty acids/non-polar tails (not tails/lipid layer)
        C: transmembrane protein/carrier protein/channel protein/intrinsic protein
   (b) (i) as lipid solubility increases, the rate increases; the membrane consists of a double layer of phospholipids; lipid soluble substances can move through the membrane more easily than water soluble substances
      (ii) small molecules diffuse faster (or converse); higher kinetic energy/easier to pass through pores/between phospholipid molecules
   (c) concentration/diffusion gradient; number of carriers/channel proteins; temperature
   (d) vitamin B1: polar/ionic;
        cannot pass through phospholipid layer/hydrophobic region;
        uses protein channels/carriers/transport proteins
        hydrophilic lining to channels;
        ref: facilitated diffusion
        Vitamin K: non-polar/non-ionic; dissolves in phospholipid/hydrophobic regions; so can pass (directly) through phospholipid/hydrophobic regions.

Enzymes

1. (a) (i) the kinetic energy increases / molecules move faster; enzyme and substrate collide more frequently; more enzyme-substrate complexes form

   (ii) tertiary / 3D structure of protein denatured / hydrogen bonds broken / active site structure altered

   (b) to prevent damage to active sites / prevent enzyme becoming denatured / enzymes would need to be constantly replaced

2. (a) (i) A: non-competitive; B: competitive

   (ii) B / competitive

   (b) (i) 5°C kinetic energy is low / few collisions between the active site of the enzyme and the substrate; 70°C the hydrogen bonds are broken as vibrations are strong / active site of the enzyme is denatured

   (ii) 1: activity of immobilised enzyme is greater between 0°C and 40°C / rate of reaction is greater

   2: optimum temp of IE covers a wider range / 40–50°C

   3: above 40°C the free enzyme begins to denature whereas the IE starts to denature at 50°C

   4: IE is more active at all temperatures except 40°C

   5: free enzyme is completely denatured at 70°C; IE is completely denatured at 80°C

   (iii) the shape of the enzyme / 3D structure is maintained or it is stabilised; molecular movement is 'reduced'

   (iv) detection of blood sugar / testing blood sugar (in diabetics)

Nucleic acids

1. (a) sugar / pentose or deoxyribose with phosphate

   (b) adenine with thymine or cytosine with guanine

   (c) hydrogen

2. (a) deoxyribose / pentose / 5C sugar

   (b) (i) A-T-A-G-C

   (ii) guanine pairs with cytosine / G pairs with C = 60% / G+C = 60%; A+T= 40% ; A= 20%.

3. (a) A: DNA; B: RNA

   (b) Nucleus / nucleolus / mitochondria / chloroplasts

   (c) Hydrogen

   (d) RNA is a short molecule; DNA is a long molecule
   Thymine (in DNA) is replaced by uracil in RNA
   DNA is a helix; RNA is a straight molecule

Cell division

1. (a) A: centriole; B: chromatid; C: centromere; D: nuclear membrane

   (b) prophase

   (c) (i) mitosis

   (ii) No crossing over / no homologous pairs / no bivalents

   (d) Asexual reproduction / repair of cells and growth

   (e) Chromatids shorter and thicker; nuclear membrane broken down; formation of spindles; centrioles at either side of cell

2. (a) metaphase

   (b) anaphase

   (c) anaphase

   (d) prophase

   (e) telophase

3. (a) (i) interphase

   (ii) ATP production / metabolically active; new organelles; protein synthesis; cell increase in size (not growth)

   (b) Doubling 20 to 40 required / DNA needs to be replicated before cell divides and then halved to maintain DNA content in two daughter cells

   (c) Two daughter cells produced with the same chromosome number in each;
   genetically identical / clones to each other; genetically identical / clone of parent cell

HB2

Biodiversity and evolution

1. (a)   Prokaryotae; Fungi; Plantae
   (b)   Class: Mammalia; Family: Hominidae
   (c) (i) Not able to interbreed; to produce fertile offspring
       (ii) DNA hybridisation; Genetic or DNA fingerprinting; (gel) electrophoresis. (NOT DNA profiling).

2. (a)   C
   (b)   F
   (c)   B
   (d)   A
   (e)   H

Uptake of energy and nutrients

1 (a)   Protein breakdown to polypeptides by pepsin in stomach; role of HCL/acid in activating pepsinogen to pepsin; polypeptides also produced by trypsin/chymotrypsin in pancreatic juice; intestinal juice contains endo- and exopeptidases; which cleave the middle of a peptide or remove the end amino group (respectively); di- and tri-peptides are digested intracellularly; or on the cell surface of the ileum epithelium; amino acids absorbed across the epithelium by a combination of diffusion and active transport; amino acids enter the capillaries in the villi.

   (b)   (Coeliac disease) caused by the presence of the protein, gluten; found in wheat/rye/barley; an enzyme in the body modifies the protein causing the immune system to react with the bowel tissue causing inflammation; villi of small intestine are flattened; interferes with absorption; symptoms range from mild: tiredness and lethargy to severe: loss of weight and acutely ill; treatment (life-long) gluten-free diet.

2. (a)   Carbohydrate: mouth; Protein: stomach; Fat: duodenum

   (b)   Exopeptidase breaks the bonds between the amino acids at the end of the polypeptide chains whereas endopeptidase breaks the bonds between the amino acids within the polypeptide.

3. (a) (i) B; (ii) B; (iii) A & D; (iv) C
   (b) (i) Absorption of fatty acids and glycerol
       (ii) Absorption of amino acids and glucose
       (iii) Move villus to change materials in contact with it
   (c)   Water is normally absorbed from the colon

Gas exchange

1. (a) (i) A: red blood cell/erythrocyte
           B: epithelial cell
       (ii) Prevents lining of alveolus sticking together; prevents alveoli collapsing; reduces surface tension; reduces cohesive nature of water molecules
       (iii) To assist breathing in premature babies
   (b) (i) Trace D is showing: 1. deeper breaths; 2. more frequent breaths
       (ii) 14
       (iii) 500 cm³
       (iv) (Tidal) volume breathed in/out would be reduced; time taken for each breath would be longer

2. (a)   Intercostal muscles contract; causing the ribs to move up and out; diaphragm contracts and flattens; volume of the thorax increases; pressure in the thorax decreases; external pressure is greater than pressure in lungs so air rushes in.

   (b)   Cigarette smoke contains tar and nicotine; tar stimulates cells (goblet) in epithelium to overproduce mucus; ciliated cells may be destroyed; resulting in a build-up of mucus; bacteria/viruses multiply resulting in chronic bronchitis; carcinogens/cancer-causing chemicals in tar; cause uncontrolled cell division/mitosis; resulting in the formation of tumours

         Carbon monoxide combines more readily with haemoglobin than oxygen; causing a reduction in the level of oxygen in the blood

Transport to and from exchange surfaces

1. (a)   D (E is also acceptable)
   (b)   Right atrium
   (c)   Muscle contracts and narrows vessel/arteriole/lumen; reduces blood flow to particular capillaries/organs/parts of body; increases pressure to other parts of the body; diverts blood flow
   (d)   Arteries are dividing up (into arterioles) with a larger surface area; blood is distributed in larger number of blood vessels with greater S.A; greater resistance due to larger S.A; more friction; distance from heart greater; large total cross-sectional area
   (e)   Enables more time to exchange materials (with tissue fluid)

2. (a) (i) 0.4 (seconds)

    (ii) Impulse spreading through ventricles; Purkinje tissue

    (iii) Contraction of atria

    (iv) (Ventricles) contract

    (v) Relaxation of ventricles

  (b) (i) Impulses not passing through damaged AVN / bundle of His / Purkyne tissue

    (ii) Heart block

    (iii) Artificial pacemaker fitted

Human defence mechanism

1. (a) Type 1: humoral; type 2: cell-mediated

(b) X: B lymphocyte; Y: T lymphocyte

(c) Bone marrow

(d) Memory cell; produces antibodies rapidly on next contact with a specific antigen or pathogen

(e) Helper, killer, suppressor, memory (any three)

(f) Helper – stimulate production of B cells; killer cells – cytotoxic; suppressor – switch off cell-mediated response at end of immune response; memory – produce antibodies on next contact with antigen.

2. (a)

	Active natural	Active artificial	Passive natural	Passive artificial
Exposure to measles	✓			
Receiving MMR vaccine		✓		
Receiving anti-rabies injection				✓
Transfer of antibodies from mother to child in breast milk			✓	

(b) The immune system is not activated; no memory cells remain; injected antibodies are short-lived

(c)(i) Clonal selection; B lymphocytes; each specific to one antigen; antigen binds to lymphocyte

  (ii) Clonal expansion; mitosis; of appropriate cell from stage 1; plasma cells; plasma cells produce antibodies; and memory cells

Pathogens, the spread of human disease and the control of infection

1. (a) Bactericidal kills / destroys bacteria

Bacteriostatic slows / stops bacteria growing / multiplying / cell division / reproducing; stops metabolism

(b) (i) Antibiotic has diffused / spread / moved into the agar; killing / inhibiting growth of bacteria

  (ii) Ampicillin

  (iii) Largest clear area; zone of inhibition; most bacteria killed in this area

(c) (Random) mutations; selection pressure favours the resistant bacteria; selective advantage; resistant bacteria survive; bacteria reproduce; form a clone to give a resistant population; pass on resistant genes

2. (a) An organism that lives (on or) in another organism; called the host; (obtains nourishment) at the expense of the host

(b) (i) Pig

  (ii) Pig becomes infected if it feeds in drainage channels / or eq. contaminated by human faeces

  (iii) By eating under-cooked infected pork

(c) (i) suckers; hooks; scolex

  (ii) A body covering that protects it from the host's immune responses; a thick cuticle; produces inhibitory substances (on the surface of the segments) to prevent digestion by the host's enzymes

(d) To overcome the problem of transfer to another host; to increase the chance of some of the offspring reaching a new host.

Index

absorption 23, 56, 58, 61, 62, 64
active
  site 26–29
  transport 21, 23, 61
adaptive radiation 47
adenine 32, 33
adenosine triphosphate (ATP) 13,
  16, 18, 22, 23, 34, 62
aerobic respiration 16
agglutination 73, 74
AIDS 98, 100
alveolus 66–67, 68, 70, 109
amino acid 9, 12, 22, 26, 27, 33, 55,
  58, 60, 61, 62, 88, 89
amphibian 50
anaemia 74–75, 108
angina 81, 84
Animalia 50
antibiotic 64, 100, 101, 104–106
antibody 12, 13, 55, 72, 73–74,
  92–96, 98
antigen 55, 73–74, 90, 92–96, 97,
  100–101, 103
arrhythmia 83
artery 67, 71, 75–78, 80–82, 84,
  88–89
asexual reproduction 35, 101–102
asthma 69, 70
atheroma 81–82, 84
atrioventricular node (AVN) 80, 83
atrium 77–80, 82–83

B lymphocyte 92–96
bacteriophage 15, 107
bacterium 15, 18, 35, 49, 59, 62,
  64, 67, 70, 72, 90–91, 94, 99,
  100–101, 103, 104–107
bile 57–58, 60
bilharzia 108
binomial system 49–50
biodiversity 46
biosensor 31
blood
  fluke 107, 108
  pressure 71, 81, 88–89
  vessel 57, 73, 76, 84, 90, 108–109
Bohr effect 86
bolus 56–58
bronchus 66, 69
buffer 28, 87
bundle of His 80

calcium 13, 63
cancer 63, 71, 93, 98
capillary 61–62, 66–67, 70, 75, 76,
  79, 86, 88, 89, 9
carbohydrate 8–9, 10, 11, 12, 17, 20,
  58, 59, 60, 61, 62
carbon dioxide, transport of 73, 87
carcinogen 71
cardiac
  cycle 77–78, 82
  muscle 77, 79, 80
carrier 99–100
  protein 12, 20–23
cell
  difference between plant and
    animal 19
  division 16, 18, 19, 34–36, 71
  membrane see plasma (cell)
    membrane
  organisation 15, 19
  wall 9, 15, 17, 18–19, 24–25, 35, 49,
    56, 104–105, 106
cellulose 8, 9, 15, 18, 25, 30 49, 56,
  62
centriole 16, 18, 19, 35
centromere 34, 35
centrosome 18
channel protein 22
chiasmata 36
chief cells 59
chitin 9, 49
chloride shift 87
chlorophyll 13, 18
chloroplast 18, 19, 49
cholera 99, 100
cholesterol 20–21, 81
Chordata 50
chromatid 34–36
chromosome 15, 16, 34–36
cisternae 17
class 48, 50
coeliac disease 64
collagen 13, 76
concentration gradient 21, 22, 23, 61
condensation 8, 10, 13, 32
conservation 46
convergent evolution 55
COPD (chronic obstructive
  pulmonary disease) 70–71
cristae 16
crossing over 36

cytokinesis 35
cytoplasm 15–19, 24, 25, 33, 35, 66,
  72
cytosine 32, 33

diaphragm 60, 66–67
diastole 77–78, 81–82
diffusion 18, 21–24, 31, 61–62,
  65–67, 72, 74, 87, 88, 104
digestion 18, 19, 56–63, 110
dipeptide 12, 58, 60, 62
diploid 34, 36
disaccharide 8, 9, 58, 60
disease 10, 15, 46, 63-64, 69–71,
  82, 84, 90, 91, 95, 96–101, 106,
  108
diverticular disease 64
DNA 15, 16, 18, 32–33, 34, 54, 55,
  63, 98, 106
drug 63–64, 69, 82, 84, 103, 105,
  106, 108–109, 110
duodenum 57–60

ecosystem 46
ectoparasite 107
egestion 56
electrocardiogram (ECG) 82–83
emphysema 69, 70
emulsification 60
endoparasite 107
endangered species 46
endemic 99, 100, 101, 108
endoplasmic reticulum (ER) 16–17,
  49
endothelium 76, 81
engulf 18, 72, 90, 91, 93, 94
enzyme
  activation energy 26
  active site 26–29
  denaturation 27, 30
  endopeptidase 58, 60
  immobilised 30–31
  induced fit model 26
  inhibition 29
  substrate 26–31
  turnover number 26, 28
epidemic 97, 99, 100
epithelial 19, 58–62, 66–67
erythrocyte 72
eukaryote 15, 49
evolution 46, 47, 48, 50–55, 65, 107

extinction 46, 50, 51, 54
exocytosis 17
exoskeleton 9
extrinsic protein 20

facilitated diffusion 21–23, 86
family 48, 50
fat 10–11, 58, 60, 61, 62, 63, 71, 80, 81, 82
fatty acid 10–11, 20, 58, 60, 62, 88
fertilisation 109
fibrous protein 13
finch 47
flaccid 25
flatworm 108
Fluid Mosaic model 20
fungi 15, 49, 99, 104, 107

gamete 34, 36
gas exchange 65–67, 85
gene 34, 36, 46, 48, 54, 105
genetic code 32, 33
genus 48
globular protein 13, 26
glucose 8–9, 14, 18, 21, 22, 31, 58, 60, 61, 62, 74, 76, 88
glycerol 10, 11, 21, 58, 60, 62
glycogen 9
glycoprotein 17, 20–21, 58, 92
glycosidic bond 8, 9, 13
goblet cell 59, 61, 66, 70
Golgi apparatus (body) 16, 17, 18, 49
granum 18
guanine 32, 33
gut (alimentary canal) 27, 56–59, 100, 108, 109, 110

habitat 13, 14, 46, 51
haem 13
haemoglobin 12, 13, 71, 72, 74–75, 85–87
haploid 34, 36
head louse 107, 111
heart 10, 71, 72, 75–84, 88–89
helix 9, 12, 32, 33, 34
heterotrophic 49, 56, 107
hexose 8
hierarchical 48
HIV 98, 101
homologous 34, 36
host 101, 102, 103, 104, 106, 107, 108, 109, 110, 111

hydrogen bond 9, 12, 14, 26–28, 32–33
hydrolysis 8, 9, 13, 58–61
hydrophilic 10, 11, 20, 22
hydrophobic 10, 11, 13, 20–21
hypertension 81–82
hypertonic 25
hypha 49
hypotonic 25

ileum 58, 59, 61
immune response 73, 90, 92–95, 110
immunity 91, 93–96
incipient plasmolysis 25
inflammation 64, 69, 90
influenza 97, 99, 101
ingestion 56, 100, 102, 109
Insecta 48
inspiration 67–68
intercellular (tissue) fluid 88
intercostal muscle 66, 67
intestine 19, 57–65, 100, 108–109
intrinsic protein 20, 21
isomer 8
isotonic 25

kinetic energy 23, 27
kingdom 48–50

lacteal (lymphatic vessel) 61–62
leucocyte see white blood cell
life cycle 101–102, 107, 109
lipid 10, 11, 12, 13, 14, 17, 18, 21, 22, 60, 62
liver 57–60, 62, 63, 101–102, 108
lung 65–71, 75, 78, 84, 85, 99, 100
lymph 57, 61, 62, 89, 93, 94, 98, 100
lymphocyte see white blood cell
lysosome 16, 17, 18, 91

malaria 99, 101–103
mammal 46, 50, 55, 67, 75, 93
matrix 16, 18, 30
meiosis 36
memory cell 93–96
metabolism 15, 26, 88
microtubule 18, 35
mineral 13, 14, 23, 58, 62, 73
mitochondrion 16, 18, 49, 61
mitosis 34–36, 93, 94, 96
monosaccharide 8, 9, 58, 60, 61
mosquito 99, 101–103

mouth 56–58, 63
mucosa 57–59
mucus 57–60, 64, 66–67, 69, 70, 90, 99, 110
multicellular 16, 19, 49, 65, 107
myocardial infarction 82
myogenic 77, 79
myoglobin 86

natural selection 47
nitrogen 12, 32, 66
non-reducing sugar 9
nuclear membrane 15, 16, 17, 35, 49
nucleic acid 13, 15, 32
nucleolus 16, 17, 18, 34, 35
nucleotide 32, 33, 55
nucleus 15, 16, 19, 25, 33, 34, 49, 72, 74

oesophagus 56, 58, 60, 63
order 48, 50
organelle 15, 16, 17, 18, 34, 49
organism 11, 13, 14, 15, 16, 19, 35, 48, 49, 55, 63, 65, 92, 95, 97, 99, 100, 101, 105, 106, 107
osmosis 9, 24–25, 89, 105
oxygen dissociation curve 85–86
oxyhaemoglobin 85–87
oxyntic cell 59

pacemaker 79, 83
pancreas 57, 59, 60
pancreatic juice 57, 60
parasite 101–103, 107–109, 111
passive transport 21, 23
pentose sugar 8, 32, 33
pepsin 59
pepsinogen 59
peptic ulcer 64
peptidase 58
peptide bond 12, 13, 58
peristalsis 56, 57, 62
pH 27, 28, 30, 58, 59, 60, 87, 90, 110
phagocytosis 72
phospholipid 11, 20–21
photosynthesis 13, 18, 49
phylogeny 52
phylum 48, 50
plasma 13, 16, 20, 22, 60, 72–74, 87–89, 93, 94, 96
plasma (cell) membrane 13, 16, 20, 22, 60, 93

plasmid 15, 106
Plasmodium 99, 101–103
plasmolysis 25
polar molecule 14, 20, 21, 22
polymer 8, 9, 30, 32, 33, 92
polynucleotide 32
polypeptide 12, 58, 59, 60, 86, 92
polysaccharide 8, 9
pork tapeworm 109–111
Prokaryotae 49
protein
  structure 12
  synthesis 17, 23, 32–33, 62, 104,
   105
Protoctista 49
pulse rate 80–81
purine 32
Purkinje (Purkyne) fibre 80, 83

red blood cell 25, 70, 72–75, 85, 87,
  91, 101–102, 108
rennin 59
resistance 76, 79, 81, 88, 90, 97,
  100, 105–106, 111
respiration 15, 16, 22, 29, 61, 62,
  65, 85
respiratory
  inhibitor 23
  surface 65
ribosome 15, 16, 17, 18, 33, 105
Rhesus 74
RNA 15, 16, 17, 32–34, 98, 101, 106
roundworm 107, 108

salivary amylase 58
Salmonella 99, 100, 105
septum 49, 77
sexual reproduction 36, 106
sinoatrial node (SAN) 79–80, 83
small intestine 19, 57–61, 64, 108,
  109
smoking 64, 70–71, 80–82
species 47–51
sphygmomanometer 81
spindle 18, 19, 34, 35

spirometer 68, 69
starch 8, 9, 18, 58, 60, 61
stomach 56–60, 63, 64, 75, 90
stroke 71, 81
sub-mucosa 57, 59
sucrose 8, 9, 14, 26, 60
surfactant 68
systole 77–78, 80–82

T lymphocyte 92, 93, 95
taxonomy 48
thylakoid 18
thymine 32, 33
tidal volume 68–69
toxin 100, 102
trachea 66, 69
transport system 17, 72
tuberculosis (TB) 99, 100
turgid 25

ultrastructure 16
unicellular 16, 19, 35, 49
uracil 32, 33
urea 62

vaccination 95–97, 100–101
valve 72, 76–79
variation 35, 36
vector 99, 101, 103
vein 67, 75–79, 83, 84, 89,
  108
ventilation 65, 67, 68
ventricle 77–83
vertebral column 50
villus 57, 60–62, 64
viral disease 101–103
virus 15, 70, 93–99, 101–103,
  106–107
vital capacity 68–69

water potential 24–25, 88–89
white blood cell 62, 63, 72–73,
  90–96, 100–101

zygote 36